T4-BBV-072

CLIMATE:
SEAS OF CHANGE

JASON Learning

 SEA RESEARCH FOUNDATION NATIONAL GEOGRAPHIC

An Education Partnership from

About JASON Learning

JASON Learning is a 501(c)(3) nonprofit organization managed by Sea Research Foundation, Inc., in partnership with the National Geographic Society. Founded in 1989 by Dr. Robert D. Ballard, the mission of JASON is to inspire and educate kids everywhere through real science and exploration. JASON provides multimedia curricular experiences in science, technology, engineering, and math (STEM) for K-12 students, and corresponding professional development for educators in a wide variety of formal and informal education environments. Each comprehensive JASON program includes reading selections, hands-on activities, videos, and online games for students, and lesson plans, implementation tips, and a powerful digital platform for educators. Live, interactive events throughout the year connect JASON participants with inspirational STEM role models. JASON's in-school curricula cover core content areas and can be used as replacements for traditional textbooks or as enriching supplemental materials. JASON's after-school offerings, which include the popular Immersion Learning program, bring the thrill of scientific discovery to students in Boys & Girls Clubs, YMCAs, 21st Century Learning Centers, and other out-of-school settings.

Visit www.jason.org to learn more about JASON, or email us at info@jason.org.

Published by JASON Learning

Requests for permission to copy or distribute any part of this work should be addressed to:

JASON Learning
Permissions Requests
55 Coogan Boulevard
Mystic, CT 06355

Phone: 888-527-6600
Fax: 703-673-1060

ISBN 978-1-935211-65-5

Printed in the United States of America by The Pyne-Davidson Company.
10 9 8 7 6 5 4 3 2 1

National Geographic and the Yellow Border are trademarks of the National Geographic Society.

Contents

Getting Started with *Climate: Seas of Change*

Developed in collaboration with our partners at Sea Research Foundation, Inc., National Geographic Society, Ocean Exploration Trust, National Oceanic and Atmospheric Administration (NOAA), Oak Ridge National Laboratory (ORNL), and other public and private organizations, *Climate: Seas of Change* is built on an "Expedition" framework to capture the energy and excitement of authentic exploration and discovery. The curriculum consists of three captivating Expeditions that provide real-world challenges, scientific background knowledge, and tools to help you complete each Expedition goal.

Let's take a closer look at the parts of each Expedition!

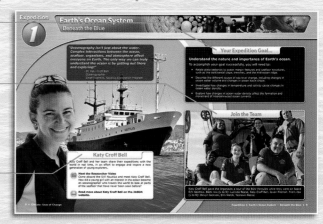

Expedition Goals

Read the Expedition goals and objectives to preview what you will be learning during the Expedition.

Join the Team

Your Expedition begins with an invitation to join the JASON Host Researcher and National Argonaut team. You will work side-by-side with this team as they guide you through your study of climate.

Host Researcher

Get to know more about the Host Researcher leading the Expedition. A video icon directs you to the Host Researcher Video, which is available on the JASON website.

Introduction Article

Once you have your Expedition goals and have met the team, you will find an introduction to "a day in the life" of the Host Researcher, and the unique work that brings this scientist face-to-face with concepts related to climate.

Expedition Briefing Video

See the adventures of the Expedition team come alive in every Expedition Briefing Video, which features the Host Researcher and Argonauts, and gives an action-packed introduction to the Expedition goals and key science concepts.

Expedition Briefing Article

The Expedition Briefing Article — which is divided into several Stages — guides you through the science of climate so you can complete your Expedition goals. Full-color graphics enhance the descriptions and explanations of essential science concepts so you can clearly see the ideas presented in each Stage.

In This Stage

On the opening page of each Stage you will find information about how to accomplish your Expedition goals and the key words you will need to learn along the way.

Try This

Try these quick and easy experiments and demonstrations to gain hands-on experience with the science topics in the Expedition.

Technology Connection

Check out the amazing tools that researchers use during their explorations in the field.

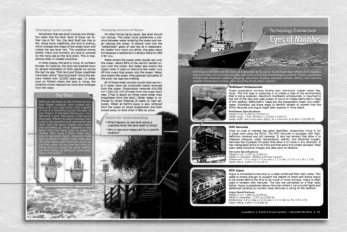

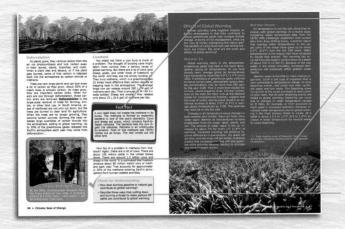

Fast Fact

Each Fast Fact contains interesting information related to the Expedition science topics.

Team Highlight

Get an up-close view of the investigations that the Host Researchers and Argonauts conducted during their field work for *Climate: Seas of Change*. Visit the JASON website to read the Argonaut journals and browse the photo galleries documenting their field experiences.

Check for Understanding

Throughout the Expedition you will find questions related to the science content. If you cannot answer a question, reread the preceding text and try again.

Expedition Lab

Put your knowledge to work with several hands-on labs in each Expedition. The labs include opportunities to practice and refine the skills you need in order to complete your Expedition goals. You will build tools, conduct investigations, collect data, and describe your observations and conclusions in your JASON Journal.

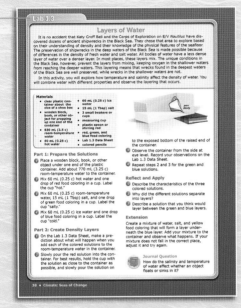

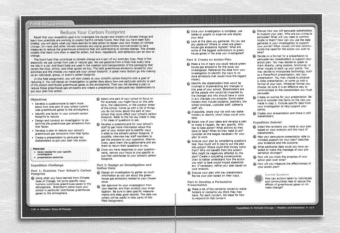

Field Assignment

A Field Assignment at the conclusion of each Expedition gives you the opportunity to put your new science skills and ideas to work in the field. You will need to accomplish the goals set out in an Expedition Challenge and then provide an analysis during your Expedition Debrief.

STEM Spotlight

Each Spotlight features the fascinating career of someone in the field of science, technology, engineering, or mathematics (STEM). You will find a short bio, photos, and a Q&A section to help you get to know the featured STEM professional and find out how you can pursue a similar career pathway.

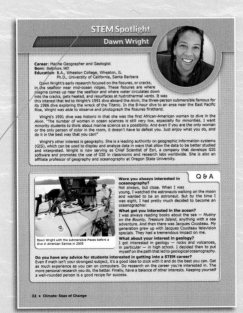

Getting Started with *Climate: Seas of Change* • 3

Tour of the JASON Expedition Center

The JASON Expedition Center is your online hub for *Climate: Seas of Change* content and resources. Your JASON experience will come to life through videos, games, your own JASON Journal, and other tools that support the Expeditions in this curriculum.

Create a Student Account

You must have online access in order to access the resources within the JASON Expedition Center. If your teacher has made an account for you, all you need to do is log into the JASON Expedition Center. Otherwise go to www.jason.org, click the login link, select "Register," and follow the instructions. Note that you will be prompted for a license key during registration. If you do not have a license key, your teacher can go to the JASON Store to purchase online access for your classroom.

JASON Expedition Center Home Page

Welcome to your JASON Expedition Center home page. From here you can quickly access all the JASON tools and resources as you begin your new Expedition. Take a moment to read the latest JASON news, search for a topic that interests you in the Digital Library, or jump right into the online version of *Climate: Seas of Change.*

Resources and Tools

Powerful online tools are always at your fingertips. Use the Digital Library to find any JASON resource quickly and easily. Save and organize your favorites in My Workspace. View assignments and community updates in your Classrooms menu. These resources and more are always accessible through the Tools menu at the top of the JASON Expedition Center page.

JASON Journal and Other Community Tools

Your student account in the JASON Expedition Center includes an online JASON Journal that allows you to take notes, write about what you have learned, and respond to journal questions as you complete each Expedition. Other Community Tools include moderated message boards and classroom home pages.

Online Version of *Climate: Seas of Change*

The entire Student Edition book of *Climate: Seas of Change* is available to you online for easy access anytime, anywhere. Log into your account to view any page from any Expedition. Click the "Listen to This" icon on the pages of the Briefing Articles to hear the text read aloud.

Team Info, Videos, and Photo Galleries

Learn more about the JASON Host Researchers and Argonauts from their biographies and journals. Video segments feature the Expedition teams in action. Photo galleries provide additional views of the researchers and Argonauts at work, as well as stunning images of climate concepts in our world.

Interactive Games

Visit the JASON Expedition Center for digital labs and games. Apply your knowledge to explore a variety of topics in climate and oceanography.

Live Events

Connect with inspiring role models in science, technology, engineering, and math (STEM) through JASON's live, interactive webcasts. Learn about STEM careers and experience actual scientific expeditions in real time. Go to www.jason.org/live to find the most up-to-date event schedule.

KATY CROFF BELL
Chief Scientist, E/V Nautilus

Your Expedition begins at **www.jason.org**

CLIMATE: SEAS OF CHANGE

Overview Video

Join your JASON Host Researchers on a journey to investigate forces that shape and change Earth's climate.

Maybe the signs that climate change is really happening are not all in tables and graphs. Maybe the signs are as simple as blossoms on a tree.

In autumn, Americans like to go "leaf peeping" to view the changing colors of the trees. But in Japan, spring is the favorite season for observing seasonal changes. *Hanami*, or "flower viewing," is a popular spring activity in Japan. And some of the favorite flowers to view are the famous cherry blossoms. Students take time from classes and workers travel as groups to see the trees. The blooming of the cherry blossoms is a time of festivals, food, music, and celebration.

Because the blooming of the cherry trees is so important in the Japanese culture, there are records of the dates when the trees bloomed going back hundreds of years. Scientists have been able to look at those records and estimate spring temperatures in Japan. And while, for hundreds of years, the temperatures varied, for the last hundred years or so the spring temperatures have crept up and the cherry trees have blossomed earlier.

The cherry blossoms in Washington, DC — trees given to the United States by Japan in 1912 — have also shown the effects of climate change. Since the National Park Service started keeping bloom-date records in 1921, the average date of peak blossoms has moved about five days earlier.

The first sighting of migrating birds returning to the northern United States from their winter homes in the tropics is a different sign of spring. For over a decade, students and other citizens have used eBird, an online database, to report the dates they have spotted birds returning in their area. Based on these data, researchers have found that, for many species of birds, warmer spring temperatures have meant an earlier migration. Is that a sign of climate change?

And is climate change the biggest threat facing polar bears? Polar bears swim from the mainland out to ice floes, where they can feed on seals. But as Earth's atmospheric and ocean temperatures increase, there are fewer ice floes. The offshore ice is melting and the polar bears must swim further out to sea. Sometimes the ice floes are too far. Sometimes the bears use up so much stored body fat that they cannot survive hibernation or nourish their young.

What Is Climate Change?

Everybody is talking about Earth's changing climate. But in order to understand climate change, you first need to understand climate. What is "climate," and how is it different from "weather"? Weather describes conditions, such as temperature and wind, at a specific place and at a moment in time. Weather describes what is happening outside your window right now. Climate is how we describe weather for a region over a long period of time. Climate describes the weather conditions you expect to experience in a given location at a given time, based on decades of experience or data.

Climate change is any significant change in the climate lasting for an extended period of time. What does climate change look like? We usually think of climate change today in terms of global warming. Global warming is the gradual increase in air temperatures near Earth's surface. On a personal level, if climate is changing, you might experience warmer temperatures at a location than you expect. Ponds may thaw earlier in the spring than they did 20 years ago. Wind or ocean current patterns might change. Precipitation may increase or decrease. Sea ice may thin or disappear. Glaciers, too. All of these observable changes are happening right now. Earth's climate is changing.

Climate changes naturally over time. However, humans also have a large role in changing Earth's climate. In *Climate: Seas of Change*, you will investigate the forces that shape — and change — climate. You will learn about the tools scientists use to understand how climate is changing, and find out what role you play today in influencing climate well into the future.

Expeditions

Helping you explore changes in Earth's climate will be a top-notch team of scientists, along with students just like you. The JASON Host Researchers and National Argonauts will take you on three Expeditions and provide you with the necessary tools to help you understand the complexities of changing climate.

In Expedition 1, you will join oceanographer Dr. Katy Croff Bell on board the Exploration Vessel (E/V) *Nautilus*. Together, you will explore Earth's ocean from shoreline to deepest trench, and begin to investigate the effects the ocean and Earth's climate have on each other.

Next, you will hop aboard the NOAA Research Vessel (R/V) *Shearwater* for Expedition 2. You will work alongside climatologists Dr. Diane Stanitski and NOAA Commander John Adler to analyze data from drifting buoys, in order to better understand the role ocean currents play in Earth's climate.

In Expedition 3, climate scientist Dr. James Hack will show you how some of the world's most advanced supercomputers are used to run climate models. Climate models are used to study the causes and potential long-term effects of climate change.

Your Challenge

In many ways, what happens with climate change is up to all of us. Most climate scientists believe that humans are contributing to climate change and global warming. It follows that it is everyone's responsibility to understand enough about climate change to be able to participate in society's response.

Climate is a product of how the sun's energy affects Earth's atmosphere, ocean, and land. We all share that same atmosphere and that same ocean. This makes climate change a global problem. And because climate change is a global problem, it will take a global solution.

You are both a global citizen and a citizen scientist. Your grasp of the facts along with your well-informed opinions about science-related issues matter, even if you are not yet old enough to vote. From choosing to reduce your carbon footprint to lobbying for clean energy, what you know about climate change can have a real impact on what you and others do in response.

As you learn more, perhaps you will be inspired to continue exploring Earth's climate and the exciting new technologies scientists are using to gather the data needed to predict future climates. There's much left to understand and many new discoveries to be made.

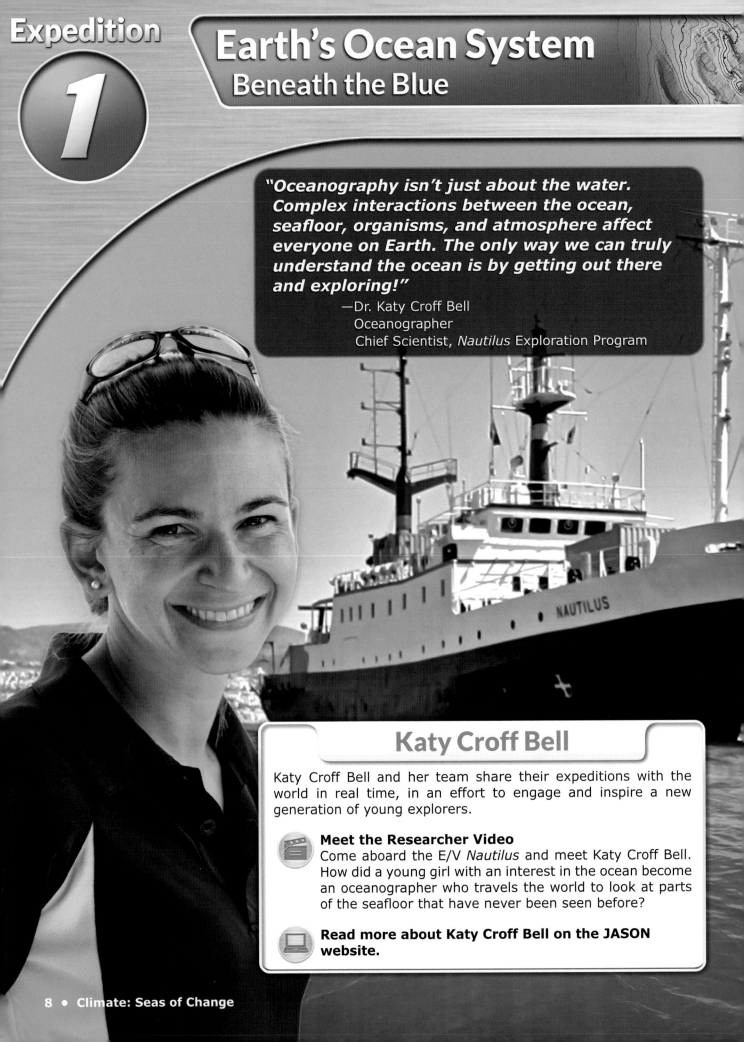

Expedition 1

Earth's Ocean System
Beneath the Blue

"*Oceanography isn't just about the water. Complex interactions between the ocean, seafloor, organisms, and atmosphere affect everyone on Earth. The only way we can truly understand the ocean is by getting out there and exploring!*"

—Dr. Katy Croff Bell
Oceanographer
Chief Scientist, *Nautilus* Exploration Program

Katy Croff Bell

Katy Croff Bell and her team share their expeditions with the world in real time, in an effort to engage and inspire a new generation of young explorers.

Meet the Researcher Video
Come aboard the E/V *Nautilus* and meet Katy Croff Bell. How did a young girl with an interest in the ocean become an oceanographer who travels the world to look at parts of the seafloor that have never been seen before?

Read more about Katy Croff Bell on the JASON website.

Your Expedition Goal...

Understand the nature and importance of Earth's ocean.

To accomplish your goal successfully, you will need to:

- Relate plate tectonics to ocean margin features and seafloor structures, such as the continental slope, trenches, and the mid-ocean ridge.

- Describe the different causes of sea level change, including changes in ocean water volume and changes in ocean basin shape.

- Investigate how changes in temperature and salinity cause changes in ocean water density.

- Explore how changes in ocean water density affect the formation and movement of interconnected ocean currents.

Join the Team

Katy Croff Bell gave the Argonauts a tour of the ROV *Hercules* while they were on board E/V *Nautilus*. Back row (L to R): Lucinda Reese, Katy Croff Bell, Jason Pittman. Front row (L to R): Devyn Jackson, Erin Walsh, Tashawn Reese.

A Great Flood

"We have to go!" When the waters of the Black Sea began to rise about 7,500 years ago, how much time did the people living near the shore have to gather their belongings and leave?

The Black Sea is an area where Earth's natural changes in climate are on display. Some 20,000 years ago, a freshwater lake existed where the Black Sea is now. Earth was still in an ice age. Global sea level was low, as water was trapped in the giant ice sheets. But then, some 12,000 years ago, the ice began to melt and sea level began to rise. The global climate changed as Earth came out of its latest ice age and readjusted to new patterns of wind, ocean currents, and temperature.

Katy Croff Bell's first expedition with explorer Robert Ballard examined the effects of sudden sea-level change in the Black Sea. In 1999, their team had found an old shoreline under 168 m (550 ft) of water along the Black Sea coast. Sediment samples and freshwater mussel shells confirmed that the Black Sea had once been cut off from the Aegean and Mediterranean seas. But then, about 7,500 years ago, salt water rushed in from the Mediterranean, drowning the old freshwater lake and changing the lives of everyone living nearby. Did the level of water rise slowly, or was there a cataclysmic rush of water, worthy of becoming the source of the Great Flood stories in many cultures?

Earth's many seas and oceans are really only one ocean. Katy Croff Bell understands how important it is to know how the ocean was created, how deep-water currents drive global energy movement, and how rising temperatures or melting glaciers can affect sea level around the globe. Do you know what goes on beneath the blue?

Expedition 1 Briefing Video

Prepare for your expedition by viewing this video clip. Learn how scientists such as Katy Croff Bell use tools and technologies to better understand the nature and importance of Earth's ocean.

In This Stage:

Your expedition goal is accomplished when you:
Know and can describe the seafloor profile.

Can explain ways in which observed sea level rises or falls.

Why this is important:
The physical features of ocean basins — including the seafloor, which is largely unseen and unexplored by humans — influence ocean currents that affect Earth's climate.

Words to identify:
continental margin, continental shelf, continental slope, turbidity current, continental rise, mid-ocean ridge, Mid-Atlantic Ridge, tectonic plate, trench, abyssal plain, seamount, abyssal hill, sea level

Stage 1: Off the Shelf

People sometimes call Earth a "blue marble" because that is what the planet looks like from space. About 70% of Earth's surface is covered by water. Almost all that water is the ocean. The atmosphere is important in shaping Earth's climate, but so is the ocean. Understanding the ocean and how thermal energy moves through it is critical to understanding Earth's climate.

Earth's ocean is billions of years old. But the ocean is not as old as Earth itself or as old as Earth's atmosphere. The atmosphere formed when gases from inside Earth were emitted through volcanoes, geysers, and hot springs. This early atmosphere contained water vapor. As Earth cooled, the water vapor in the atmosphere condensed and rained down on the young planet, forming the ocean. This probably occurred at least 4 billion years ago.

Earth's ocean is divided into five named oceans: Atlantic, Pacific, Indian, Arctic, and Southern. But if you look at a map, it is clear that Earth has just one, interconnected ocean. The ocean contains almost 97% of Earth's water, but it is all too salty to drink.

Features of the Ocean Floor

Beneath the ocean is the seafloor. Like the land you can see on the continents, the ocean floor has topographic features, such as valleys and mountains. Parts of the ocean floor are flat. Other parts are not. Scientists divide the ocean floor into three major regions: the continental margins, the mid-ocean ridges, and the deep-ocean basins. Let's look at these three regions in greater detail.

Continental Margins

The **continental margin** is the relatively shallow water area closest to the continents. It is made up of three parts: the continental shelf, the continental slope, and the continental rise.

The **continental shelf** is the shallowest part of the ocean floor and is closest to the shoreline. The width of the continental shelf varies from less than 100 m all the way up to 1,500 km (328 ft to 932 mi). The depth of the water over the shelf ranges from zero at the shoreline to around 135 m (443 ft). The continental shelf is generally flat. How flat is the continental shelf? The slope of the shelf is only about one-tenth of a degree. Most parking lots have more slope than that!

At the edge of the continental shelf is the slope break, which is the boundary between the continental shelf and the **continental slope**. If you were to take a submersible to the slope break, you would see the ocean floor dropping off below you. The continental slope is the sloping surface seaward of the continental shelf.

Fast Fact

Large amounts of sediment suddenly moving down the continental slope can form what are called turbidity currents. A **turbidity current** is a mix of water and sediment that can travel like an avalanche down the slope at speeds of up to 80 km/h (50 mph). Turbidity currents not only distribute massive amounts of sediment, but they can also erode the seafloor. V-shaped submarine canyons, cut into the continental slope and back into the shelf, are formed by turbidity currents. Some submarine canyons are very long and deep. The Monterey Canyon off the coast of California is about the same size as the Grand Canyon! Having a submarine canyon so near to shore allows California ocean explorers to study deep-sea features and eco-systems more easily.

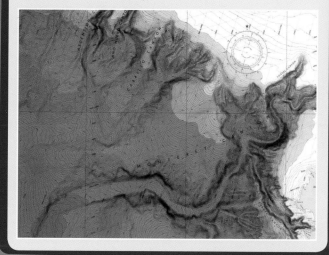

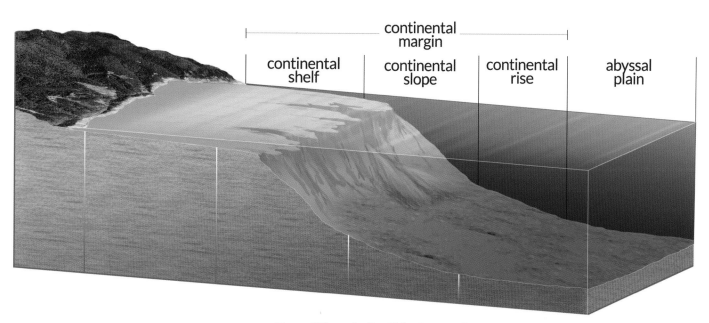

continental margin

| continental shelf | continental slope | continental rise | abyssal plain |

Peeking Into the Abyss

Imagine the early sailors, sailing their ships across the seas from continent to continent, from home to distant port. Those sailors would have known a lot about their own harbors. They would have known which way to leave their home port, where to find the safe, deep channels, and where to avoid the treacherous shallows. They might have known the same details about their destination and certain points in between. But for vast expanses of ocean, the sailors would have had no clue as to what they were sailing over. "Here there be monsters," their charts might have said. How and when did the deep and mysterious ocean floor give way to the detailed seafloor maps we see today?

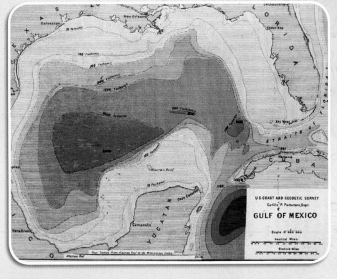

Sounding

In very shallow water, a person on a boat might be able to touch bottom with a long pole. For slightly deeper water, sailors centuries ago developed a way to take soundings. A sounding is a depth measurement. Early soundings were performed by lowering a weight attached to a rope over the side of the ship until the weight touched bottom. The rope was marked in fathoms, a unit measured as the distance between a sailor's outstretched arms. Later, fathoms were standardized to equal 6 ft (1.83 m) and the rope was replaced with steel piano wire.

The first bathymetric contour map of the Atlantic Ocean seafloor was created in 1855 by Matthew Maury, director of the U.S. Navy's Depot of Charts. Maury used sounding data from Navy vessels and whaling ships to create his map. Maury had plenty of data for coastal areas where the water was shallow, but only 200 soundings for areas where the water was deeper than 1,000 fathoms (6,000 ft or 1,829 m). Even with these few data points, Maury was the first person to identify an undersea ridge in the middle of the Atlantic. He called the ridge "Middle Ground." Scientists would later find that "Middle Ground" was the Mid-Atlantic Ridge.

Sonar

Clearly the original soundings had nothing to do with sound. However, that changed with the advent of sonar and echo sounding technology. With sonar, sound waves are used to measure the distance between the ship at the ocean's surface and the ocean floor below. Sound pulses (called pings) travel from the ship down through the water, bounce off the ocean floor, and then travel back through the water to receivers on the ship. The shallower the water, the shorter the ping's travel time. Water depth is calculated using the total time it takes for a ping to make the round trip from ship to seafloor and back to the ship. Calculations also use the density of the water (or even different densities, depending on how much water the sound waves travel through), and the speed at which sound travels through that density of water.

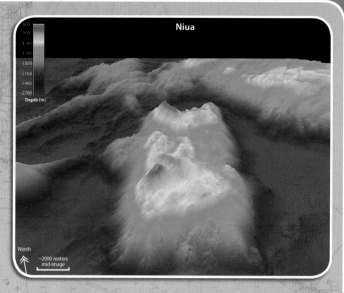

Ships used single-beam sonar to make the first bathymetric maps of the ocean floor, starting in the 1930s. Those maps, however, could only be as good as the paths taken by the ships as they gathered data. It was impossible to crisscross the ocean enough times to "see" everything below. Depth data from single-beam sonar can also be inaccurate. There are uncertainties that arise from the movement of the ship. Other inaccuracies can occur because of underwater currents with different water temperatures and salinities.

Today, computers allow ships to use multi-beam sonar systems that send out hundreds of sound beams in a wide swath and allow a ship to map more of the seafloor with each pass. Detailed sound velocity profiles are taken periodically by lowering an instrument overboard and taking readings of depth versus temperature, salinity, and pressure. This allows depth calculations to correct for refraction that occurs when sound moves through one density of seawater and enters another.

Some research vessels are equipped with another type of mapping system called sidescan sonar, in which a device is towed behind the ship. Sidescan sonar maps differences in the density of things on the seafloor. Katy Croff Bell, Robert Ballard, and other researchers use both sidescan and multi-beam sonar systems on E/V *Nautilus* to explore for shipwrecks, map ocean-floor habitats, and investigate other unknown features on the seafloor.

Satellites

Scientists on ships cannot simply "peer through" the ocean water using radio waves or radar. Radio waves are absorbed by water. However, researchers have found that they can map the seafloor by taking their instruments into orbit. Radar on Earth-orbiting satellites can be used to measure the tiny variations in the elevation of the ocean's surface. These small highs and lows correspond to highs and lows on the ocean floor, hundreds or thousands of meters below.

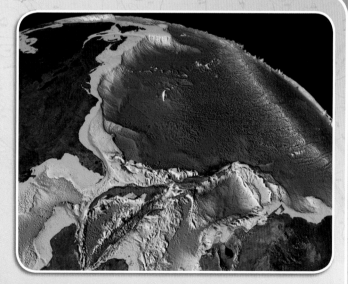

While bathymetric maps made from satellite data are not as accurate as multi-beam sonar bathymetric maps, the satellite maps can cover large areas and show seafloor topography in areas too remote or too challenging for ship-based mapping. For example, these satellite maps have revealed all volcanoes on the seafloor greater than 1,000 m (3,281 ft) tall. Roughly half of these volcanoes had never been charted before by traditional sounding or sonar mapping.

The continental slope is not steeply sloped. At an average of 3 degrees, it is simply sloped a lot more than either the continental shelf above or the deep-ocean floor below, called the abyssal plain. Even this small angle is enough that sediment does not build up on the slope. If sediment reaches the continental slope, it slides down toward the deep-ocean basin. The **continental rise** is an irregular surface found at the base of the continental slope. It separates the slope from the abyssal plain. The continental rise is formed by sediment and large blocks of material sliding down the continental slope and accumulating at the base of the slope.

> ## ✓ Check for Understanding
>
> - Name the three parts of the continental margin.
> - What is the flattest part of the continental margin?

Mid-Ocean Ridges

Perhaps the most impressive — and at one point entirely unknown — geographic feature under the ocean is the mid-ocean ridge. The **mid-ocean ridge** is a continuous range of underwater mountains that wraps around Earth like the seam of a baseball. The entire length of the mid-ocean ridge is almost 75,000 km (46,600 mi) — close to double Earth's circumference. The **Mid-Atlantic Ridge** is the mid-ocean ridge that runs north to south down the middle of the Atlantic Ocean.

If you take a closer look at the mid-ocean ridge, you will see that it has an average height of 2.5 km (1.5 mi). A central rift valley runs down the middle. The rift valley can be as wide as 30 km (20 mi) and as deep as 3 km (2 mi).

A hydrothermal vent is a place where ocean water seeps down into the seafloor, gets heated up and enriched in minerals by magma that is close to the seafloor surface, and then circulates back out into the ocean from cracks in Earth's crust. This black smoker is a hydrothermal vent located deep in the Pacific Ocean.

It is here, in the rift valley, that new ocean crust is formed as two of Earth's tectonic plates diverge, or move apart. (A **tectonic plate** is a large slab of Earth's hard outer layer that moves over the more putty-like layer beneath.) The mid-ocean ridge is where the seafloor spreads apart. There are volcanic eruptions, hydrothermal vents, and frequent small earthquakes. The mid-ocean ridge is broken in places by faults that shift the ridge sideways.

Ocean Trenches

Think back to what you already know about plate tectonics. Recall that a plate boundary is a place where two tectonic plates meet. The mid-ocean ridge forms where two plates diverge, or move apart. A trench sometimes forms where two plates converge, or come together.

A **trench** is a long, narrow depression that occurs at a convergent plate boundary when an oceanic plate subducts beneath, or moves under, another oceanic plate or a continental plate.

mid-ocean ridge

oceanic crust

lithosphere

rising magma

asthenosphere

▲ The pilot chamber inside the *DEEPSEA CHALLENGER* is a small sphere, only 109 cm (43 in.) wide. The chamber is so small that James Cameron had to keep his knees bent and could barely move.

The plate that subducts — along with the sediment it carries with it — slowly descends into Earth's upper mantle and is eventually melted and recycled into new rock.

Trenches continue to be mysterious features due to their size and depth. Since tectonic plates are so large and since trenches form at convergent plate boundaries, most of the deep-ocean trenches are very long. For example, the Peru-Chile trench is about 5,900 km (3,666 mi) long and runs two-thirds the length of South America. Deep-ocean trenches average between 50 and 120 km (31 and 75 mi) in width.

But the most striking and mysterious dimension of a deep-ocean trench is its depth. The deepest parts of the ocean are in these trenches. Challenger Deep, a part of the Mariana Trench, is the deepest known point at close to 11 km (6.8 mi) below sea level. How deep is that? Compare that depth with the height of Mt. Everest, Earth's tallest mountain. Everest is "only" about 8.8 km (5.5 mi) above sea level.

If you were to go to the bottom of the Mariana Trench, you would experience water pressure over 1,000 times greater than the air pressure you experience on land! And yet, explorers have gone down into the trench. The first descent to the bottom of the Mariana Trench was in 1960 when Swiss oceanographer and engineer Jacques Piccard and U.S. Navy Lieutenant Don Walsh were lowered in the bathyscaphe *Trieste*. In 2012, James Cameron — National Geographic Explorer-in-Residence and director of movies such as *The Terminator, Titanic,* and *Avatar* — descended to the bottom of the Mariana Trench in a one-person submersible called *DEEPSEA CHALLENGER*.

trench

continental crust

subduction zone   rising magma

Deep-Ocean Basins

The deep-ocean basin is mostly covered by abyssal plains where the water depths average between 4,500 and 6,000 m (14,800 and 19,700 ft). The abyssal plains are also very flat. They have a slope of less than one degree. The reason they are so flat is that fine sediment has drifted down to the seafloor over millions of years, building up a thick blanket of material that covers most irregularities in the seafloor. Abyssal plains are more common in the Atlantic and Indian Oceans, where more fine sediment is able to reach the deep-ocean basin. Abyssal plains are less common in the Pacific Ocean because sediment there is often deposited into the deep-ocean trenches found along the Pacific Ocean rim.

Undersea Mountains

Volcanic mountains scatter the ocean floor. Many of them formed at mid-ocean ridges and have been carried away from the ridge as new ocean crust forms and the seafloor spreads apart. Others form at subduction zones when the subducted plate melts and the resulting magma rises through the plate above. Still others formed over hotspots in Earth's mantle. Some of these underwater volcanic mountains are tall enough to reach above the water where they form volcanic islands, such as the Hawaiian Islands or other islands in the Pacific Ocean, Caribbean Sea, and Aegean Sea.

One of the best parts of Katy Croff Bell's job is finding something new and unexpected. Take for example her exploration of the underwater volcano Kolumbo, in the Aegean Sea near Santorini. (Santorini itself is a famous volcano. Its eruption approximately 3,600 years ago was enormous, and possibly contributed to the collapse of the Minoan civilization on Crete.) Kolumbo erupted in 1650 AD, releasing poisonous gases that killed people on Santorini. GPS measurements suggested that Kolumbo might be building up for another eruption, warranting further study. What E/V *Nautilus* researchers did not expect to find when they sent their ROVs down into the crater was an extensive hydrothermal vent system unlike any they had seen before.

Something was definitely different about the Kolumbo vents, according to Katy Croff Bell. "Many of the hydrothermal vents in the world have large crabs or tubeworms and fish and lots of different organisms living on them." That was not the case at Kolumbo. "We noticed that there were no fish or other organisms that lived inside this volcano and we wondered why. So we collected some of the water that was coming out of the hydrothermal vents and found that it was very, very high in carbon dioxide, which creates a toxic environment for these animals." The Kolumbo vents release hot water as well as bubbles of carbon dioxide. The carbon dioxide dissolves in the water, making it acidic and dense. The crater is enclosed, so the dense water does not get out, and water containing oxygen does not get in. That is why, unlike at other hydrothermal vent sites, there are no fish or other animals near the Kolumbo vents — just bacteria abundant enough to cloud the water and coat the mineral vent chimneys.

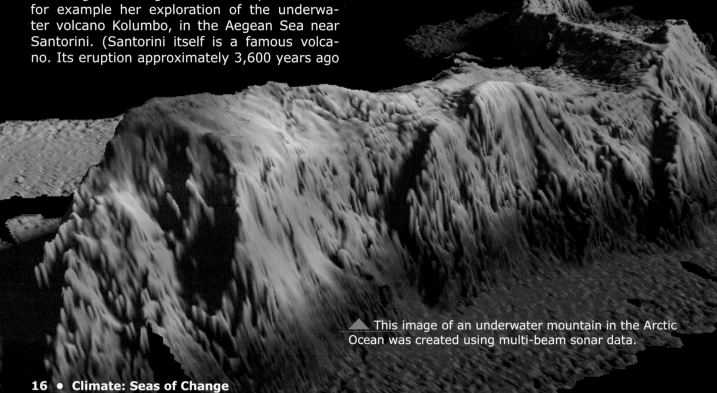

This image of an underwater mountain in the Arctic Ocean was created using multi-beam sonar data.

Seamounts are undersea mountains that are at least 1 km (0.6 mi) tall, but are not tall enough to reach the ocean's surface. Most seamounts are volcanic in origin. There are at least 100,000 seamounts scattered across the ocean floor. While some seamounts are known by fishermen and valued for their rich ecosystems, others are still unknown and unmapped, even today. In 2005, a U.S. Navy submarine ran into an uncharted seamount in the Pacific Ocean, south of Guam, sustaining heavy damage and one casualty.

One chain of seamounts is found in the Atlantic Ocean, several hundred kilometers off the East Coast of the United States and north of Bermuda. Called the New England Seamounts, they are known for their deep-sea corals and have been studied for signs of changes in deep-ocean currents that might affect global climate. The Emperor Seamounts in the Pacific Ocean are an extension of the Hawaiian Island chain.

Fast Fact

One seamount that is not a submerged volcano is the Eratosthenes Seamount, located in the Mediterranean Sea south of Cyprus. Eratosthenes is thought to be a piece of the African continent that has been ripped away and is slowly being subducted beneath the Eurasian Plate to the north. The top of the seamount has an area of 9,600 km² (3,700 mi²) — almost the size of the island of Jamaica. Katy Croff Bell and the Corps of Exploration on E/V *Nautilus* studied the seamount on two recent expeditions. Among other things, they found evidence that large depressions on the seamount's flat top are actually sinkholes formed when the top of the seamount was above sea level some 6 million years ago.

▲ The *Nautilus* team also found several shipwrecks on the seamount, including Eratosthenes C, which is estimated to be 2,300 to 2,500 years old. The ancient ceramic storage containers pictured here are part of the wreck's enormous debris field.

Submerged mountains that are shorter than seamounts are called **abyssal hills**. And though you have probably never heard of abyssal hills, they are an incredibly abundant feature. There are hundreds of thousands of abyssal hills covering much of the ocean floor. Some stick up from the seafloor as rounded hills a few hundred meters tall. Others have been covered over by layers of seafloor sediment.

✓ Check for Understanding
● Where is new ocean floor formed?
● Which ocean floor feature occurs at a divergent plate boundary?
● Which ocean floor feature occurs at a convergent plate boundary?

Sea Level

Sea level has changed in more places than just the Black Sea. Over geologic time, sea level has risen and fallen as Earth has gone through multiple stages of mountain-building, ice ages, and the thaws that inevitably followed.

What do we mean by the term "sea level"? **Sea level** is the average level of the ocean's surface where it strikes land at a specific location. But why "at a specific location"? If all of Earth's seas and oceans are part of the same grand ocean, it seems that sea level should be the same everywhere on Earth. But that is not true. Why does sea level appear to vary from place to place?

One reason sea level differs is because of tides. Fluctuations of the tides make sea level rise and fall each day. Tidal sea level changes depending on the time of day, the time of month, the location, and the particular geography of the coast.

Because of the way Earth spins on its axis, sea level is higher along shorelines on the western side of ocean basins. Picture partially filling the spaces of an empty ice cube tray with water. If you were to shift the entire tray to your right, water would appear to slosh to the left, making the water level higher on the left side of each cube space than on the right. Earth's constant spinning creates a continuous slosh!

Changing Land Levels

Remember that sea level involves two things: the water and the land. Each of these can either rise or fall. Yes, the land itself can rise or fall. Along some coastlines, the land is sinking, which changes the shape of the ocean basin and makes the sea level rise. The coastline moves farther inland and formerly dry land is covered by the rising sea as the land sinks. This is happening today in coastal Louisiana.

In other places, the land is rising. In northern Europe, for instance, the land was pushed down by several kilometers of thick glacial ice during the last ice age. That land and those coastlines have been slowly "bouncing back" since the glaciers melted over 10,000 years ago. In areas such as Finland where the land is rising, the coastline moves seaward as more land emerges from the water.

Changing Amount of Water

All other things being equal, sea level should not change. The water cycle establishes a balance between water entering the ocean and water leaving the ocean. It should work like the "bottomless" glass of iced tea at a restaurant. No matter how much you drink, the glass stays full because a waitperson is always there to refill it for you.

Water enters the ocean when clouds rain over the ocean. About 80% of the world's rainfall occurs over the ocean. But water also enters the ocean when it rains on land and the water runs off into rivers that empty into the ocean. Water also enters the ocean when glaciers and parts of the polar ice caps are melting.

All of these water sources would raise sea level if water were not continually being removed from the ocean. Evaporation removes 434,000 km^3 (104,122 mi^3) of water from the ocean each year. (That is about six times more water than evaporates from the land.) Other water is removed by direct freezing of water at high latitudes. Water at Earth's poles is also removed from the ocean by direct evaporation and then locked away on land when it falls as snow.

Try This!

Hold your left hand up flat in front of your face, fingers together, palm toward you. Now, with your right hand, hold a pencil so that it is horizontal across the base of your fingers on the hand facing you. Your left hand is land. The pencil is the top of the ocean. Where the pencil touches your hand is the shoreline and represents sea level. Hold the pencil steady and move your left hand up. What happens to sea level? Move the hand back to where it started. Then move it down. What happens to sea level? Again, move the hand back to where it started. Now, hold your left hand steady and move the pencil up and then down. Do you see how rising or falling land can cause the same relative sea level change as falling or rising water level in the ocean?

Check for Understanding

- What happens to sea level along a coastline when the land itself is rising?
- Why is sea level measured for a specific location?

When Katy Croff Bell and the Corps of Exploration go to sea on board Exploration Vessel (E/V) *Nautilus*, they know they are on a ship equipped with some of the latest technological systems. Primary capabilities include high-resolution seafloor mapping, advanced remotely operated vehicles (ROVs), and real-time satellite transmission of data. Here are a few of the ship's systems:

Multibeam Echosounder

Ocean exploration involves finding new, previously unseen ocean features. The first step in exploring is to create a map of the environment that is being explored. *Nautilus's* multibeam echosounder is mounted to the hull of the ship and uses pulses of sound to create bathymetric maps of the seafloor. Bathymetric maps are like topographic maps, but underwater. Scientists use these maps to identify targets of interest that the ROVs *Hercules* and *Argus* might later explore in more detail.

Multibeam Specifications
Weight in air: 8,200 kg (18,000 lb)
Depth range: 7,000–10,000 m (23,000–33,000 ft)
Swath width: five times water depth, to a maximum of 8,000 m (26,000 ft)

ROV *Hercules*

Once an area of interest has been identified, researchers move in for a closer look using the ROVs. The ROV *Hercules* is equipped with high-definition video and still cameras. It also has sensors that allow it to measure pressure, water temperature, salinity, and dissolved oxygen. *Hercules* has hydraulic thrusters that allow it to move in any direction. It has manipulator arms on its front end that allow it to collect samples. Fiber optic cable transmits images and data back to *Nautilus*.

***Hercules* Specifications**
Weight in air: 2,450 kg (5,400 lb)
Weight in seawater: Slightly positively buoyant
Dimensions: 3.9 m long x 1.9 m wide x 2.2 m tall (12.8 ft x 6.2 ft x 7.2 ft)
Depth rating: 4,000 m (13,124 ft)

ROV *Argus*

Argus is connected to the ship by a steel-reinforced fiber optic cable. This cable is strong enough to support the weight of *Argus* and allows *Argus* to be towed behind the ship to do visual or sonar surveys. *Argus* is often used in tandem with *Hercules*. The two are connected by a fiber optic tether. *Argus* is positioned above *Hercules* where it can provide lights and additional cameras to monitor what *Hercules* is doing on the seafloor.

***Argus* Specifications**
Weight in air: 1,800 kg (4,000 lb)
Weight in seawater: 1,350 kg (3,000 lb)
Dimensions: 3.8 m long x 1.2 m wide x 1.3 m tall (11 ft x 4 ft x 4 ft)
Depth rating: 6,000 m (19,686 ft)

Mapping the Ocean Floor

Katy Croff Bell knows that maps play an important role in ocean exploration. The Corps of Exploration on board E/V *Nautilus* uses sonar systems to create bathymetric maps of the seafloor wherever the ship is exploring. Studying these maps could reveal previously undiscovered seamounts, underwater volcanoes, or other seafloor features. Bell and her team use the maps to identify interesting places to investigate more closely.

In this activity, you will create a model of an ocean floor feature. You will make a bathymetric map of your model. Then you will look at other students' maps and will attempt to identify the types of features they represent.

Materials
- plastic container, at least 20 cm (8 in.) tall
- ruler
- masking tape
- Modeling Ocean Floor Features Card
- waterproof modeling clay
- foam board
- paper metric ruler
- sheet of acetate
- scissors
- pitcher of tinted water
- cup
- fine-tip permanent marker

Part 1: Create a Model

1. Measure 15 cm (6 in.) straight up from the bottom of a plastic container, and use a piece of masking tape to make a line at this level on the side of the container. Label the line "sea level."

2. Tape a paper metric ruler to the outside of the plastic container, with the zero end of the ruler at the sea level line. Remember that bathymetric maps show depths below sea level, and larger numbers represent deeper features.

3. Look at your Modeling Ocean Floor Features Card. If necessary, go back to Expedition 1 Stage 1 and re-read the description of your feature. Use the websites provided by your teacher to look at some images showing examples of your feature.

4. Sculpt a model of your feature using clay, and place your model into the plastic container. Be sure to follow the size guidelines on your Modeling Ocean Floor Features Card. If you are modeling a submarine canyon, you can use clay to create the shape of the canyon and then use a piece of foam board on each side of the canyon to create the continental slope.

5. Cut the acetate to fit over the top of your container. Tape the acetate to the container, leaving a small gap on one side for pouring water into the container.

6. Predict what a bathymetric map of your model will look like. Will the lines be close together or far apart? Explain. Will the distances between pairs of lines be different in different parts of the map? Explain.

Part 2: Create a Bathymetric Map

1. You will now create a bathymetric map of your model. Begin by looking directly down through the acetate at the clay model. Carefully trace the outline of the model's lowest elevation (where it touches the bottom) onto the acetate using the permanent marker.

2. Read the depth of the bottom of the model from the paper metric ruler, and record the depth on the line you drew.

3. Carefully pour the colored water into the container through the gap until it reaches a level 1 cm above the bottom of the container.

4. Again look down through the acetate at the model. Carefully draw a line to show where the colored water meets the model.

5. Continue adding 1 cm-thick layers of water, one layer at a time. For each layer you add, draw a new line where the water and model meet. For every two lines you draw, read the depth on the paper metric ruler and record the depth on the line. Keep adding water and drawing lines until you have reached the top of the model.

6. Remove the map from the top of your container. Then place your container and model along with all your classmates' models on a large table. If your model is not clearly visible because of the water, remove the water from the container before displaying your model.

7. Exchange bathymetric maps with a classmate, and use your new map to identify which model your classmate made.

Reflect and Apply

1. Describe the bathymetric map you created and explain how it relates to the ocean floor feature model you created. How well does your map match the prediction you made at the end of Part 1?

2. How did you identify the model that matched your classmate's bathymetric map? What clues did the map give you?

3. What ocean floor feature do you think your classmate's map and model represent? Explain.

Extension

View a bathymetric map of the ocean floor, such as the map below of the area around the underwater volcano Kolumbo. Select a feature on the map, and use clay to model the feature based on the map. Write a brief paragraph explaining how you interpreted the map and why the model looks the way it does.

 Journal Question

Why is it important to map the ocean floor?

Your expedition goal is accomplished when you:

Know the physical properties of seawater.

Can explain how salinity and temperature affect the density of seawater.

Why this is important:

Understanding the physical properties of seawater is necessary for understanding how the ocean helps absorb excess carbon dioxide from Earth's atmosphere and redistributes thermal energy via ocean currents.

Words to identify:

salinity, turbidity, pH, buffer, ocean acidification, density, mixed layer, thermocline, deep water layer, thermal expansion, specific heat, heat capacity

Stage 2: The Scoop On Seawater

How do you know when something unusual is going on thousands of meters below you on the seafloor? That is a question we put to Katy Croff Bell. "The properties of seawater play a very large role in the exploration we do on *Nautilus*." Talking about her team's use of instruments on the ROV *Hercules*, she added, "When we go out, we have an idea of what the average water temperature is in an area, what the average salinity is, the dissolved oxygen... Whenever we see anomalies, or differences from these averages, then we suspect there might be something interesting happening on the seafloor."

Properties of Seawater

Water properties are important to researchers on *Nautilus*. Those same properties are also critical in looking at climate change. Let's look at water properties and how those properties are important in understanding seawater and the ocean.

In many ways, water is water, no matter where you find it. Water in the ocean shares physical properties with water in lakes and streams. For instance, water can dissolve more substances than any other liquid. Water occurs as a gas, liquid, and solid all within Earth's normal range of temperatures. But there's one obvious way in which ocean water is different than water in a lake or stream.

Salinity

Even if you have never been to the ocean, you know that seawater is salty. The salty taste of seawater means there are more materials dissolved in seawater than you might find in tap water or in the fresh water of a lake or river. This does not mean water in a river or even water coming out of your kitchen sink faucet is free of dissolved materials. Fresh water just contains much less dissolved material than the salt water in the ocean.

Salinity is a measurement of the amount of dissolved material or salts in a liquid. Salinity is typically measured in parts per thousand (ppt). On average, seawater contains about 35 g of dissolved salt in every 1,000 g of water. That is a salinity of 35 ppt, or 3.5%. That is roughly the same salinity you would get if you were to dissolve two tablespoons of table salt in one liter of tap water. The ocean's average salinity of 35 ppt is about 220 times saltier than the fresh water in a river or stream.

Salinity is a measure of just the dissolved salt content of seawater. It is not a measure of suspended solids such as the sand, silt, and clay-sized sediment entering the ocean from rivers. Salinity measurements also do not include organic solids such as phytoplankton or bacteria.

Try This!

Add 10 mL (2 tsp) table salt to 60 mL (1/4 c) warm water. Use a clean craft stick to stir until you can no longer see the salt. What happened to the solid salt? The salt is not really gone — it is just dissolved in the water. Dip the craft stick in the water and taste it if you have any doubts. Now pour the salty water out onto a dark plate and set the plate aside overnight. Take a look at the plate the next day. What happened to the water? Describe what you see left behind on the plate.

Source of the Ocean's Salt

The substance you know as table salt is the chemical compound sodium chloride. When sodium chloride dissolves in water, it separates into sodium and chloride ions. Sodium and chloride ions make up just over 85% of the dissolved salts in seawater. Seawater also contains sulfate, magnesium, calcium, and potassium ions, as well as small amounts of other dissolved materials such as metals.

Where did all the salt and other dissolved materials in the ocean come from? Many of the substances in seawater came from the weathering

Team Highlight

Katy Croff Bell shows the Argonauts a Niskin bottle, one of several different devices used by researchers on the E/V *Nautilus* to collect deep-water samples.

of rock on Earth's continents. Some of the substances came from undersea volcanic eruptions and hydrothermal vents on the seafloor.

Scientists believe the total salt content of the ocean has not changed much in the last 100 million years. The ocean has reached a balance between salt entering and leaving the water. For example, more than 3 billion metric tons of salt enter Earth's atmosphere each year when waves break, forming sea spray that releases tiny salt particles into the air. Other salt becomes part of the seafloor sediment or nearshore salt deposits. By some estimates, if you could take all the salt out of the ocean, dry it, and spread it on all Earth's continents, it would form a layer 166 m (545 ft) thick. That is nearly as tall as a 40-story building!

Changing Water's Salinity

Remember, we said the average salinity of seawater is about 35 ppt. But the measured salinity of seawater can range from 33 to 37 ppt. How does seawater get less salty or more salty?

Let's start with lowering water's salinity. It is very hard to remove the dissolved salts from water. But adding more water — water that is fresh or at least has a lower salinity — will dilute the solution. If you have the same amount of salt in a greater volume of water, the salinity will be lower. Water at the ocean's surface can have lower salinity in areas such as the tropics where there is significant rainfall. And seawater near the mouth of a river also has lower salinity. The freshwater runoff from the land dilutes the salt water in the ocean near the river's mouth.

One way to increase the salinity of the ocean would be to add more dissolved salts. Another way to increase the salinity is via evaporation. When seawater evaporates, the water vapor leaves behind the dissolved salts, making the remaining water saltier. Just ask the Corps of Exploration on the E/V *Nautilus*. Katy Croff Bell says, "When we go swimming in the eastern Mediterranean Sea, the water is so salty it burns our eyes!" If you have the same amount of salt in a smaller volume of water, the salinity will be higher. Similarly, when seawater freezes, small amounts of the dissolved salts get trapped in the ice. The remaining salts are left behind in the surrounding water, increasing that water's salinity.

Check for Understanding

- How can seawater become less salty?
- Describe three ways to increase the salinity of seawater.

Turbidity

Like water in a pond, seawater can be clear, cloudy, or somewhere in-between. **Turbidity** is a measurement of how cloudy or clear water is. The more sediment or other suspended particles in the water, the less light can be transmitted through the water. The water appears cloudy because the light entering the water scatters. You cannot see through the water. (Picture looking for a spoon at the bottom of a sink filled with clean water. Now picture looking for the same spoon after a cup of milk has been added to the water.) The cloudier the water appears, the greater the turbidity.

▲ One way to measure turbidity is with a Secchi disk. The disk is lowered into the water and observed as it sinks. The greater the water's turbidity, the shallower the depth at which the disk seems to disappear.

There are several things that can increase the turbidity of seawater. Sediment pouring into the ocean from a river can raise turbidity. Sand settles out of water quickly, but fine sediment like clay or silt takes much longer to settle to the seafloor. Strong storms or bottom-feeding animals, such as crabs and flatfish, can stir up fine sediment in shallow ocean water, increasing turbidity. Sometimes the addition of extra nutrients to water near shore can cause an algal bloom — a sudden increase in the number of algae in the water near the surface. Algal blooms can also increase turbidity.

Turbidity is an important water quality to measure because it affects organisms that live in the shallow ocean water. Aquatic plants and algae rely on sunlight to make energy; they are less productive when increased turbidity causes them to get less sunlight. Other organisms that depend on these producers for food and oxygen are also affected.

Turbidity also affects water temperature. Scattered sunlight is absorbed by suspended particles in the water. This is why increases in the turbidity of water can also increase the temperature.

Dissolved Gases

Seawater also contains dissolved gases. The concentration of dissolved gases in water depends on water temperature, salinity, and pressure. The greater the water temperature, the less dissolved gas the water can hold. Also, the greater the salinity of seawater, the less dissolved gas the water can hold. For example, seawater can hold about 20% less oxygen than fresh water at the same temperature and pressure. The movement of water can increase its ability to hold dissolved gases. Think about how

stirring a cup of tea helps dissolve a spoonful of sugar. In a similar way, wind and waves that mix the ocean's surface water can help increase the amount of dissolved gases in the water.

Water at higher pressure, such as seawater at greater depth, is able to hold more dissolved gas. Picture a bottle of ginger ale. When you pop the top of the bottle, you release the pressure in the bottle. Bubbles of gas appear in the liquid. At the new, lower pressure, the ginger ale is not able to hold as much carbon dioxide in solution.

Dissolved oxygen in seawater comes from the atmosphere as well as from the life processes of aquatic plants and plant-like organisms such as green algae. The algae that live in shallow water use sunlight to make their own food through the process of photosynthesis, which also releases oxygen into the water. For these reasons, levels of dissolved oxygen are highest near the ocean's surface. Of course, there is still a lot more oxygen in the air than in the water. But the oxygen that is in the water is critical to life in the ocean.

Seawater also contains dissolved carbon dioxide. Unlike oxygen, carbon dioxide is much more plentiful in seawater than it is in Earth's atmosphere. The same photosynthesizing algae

◀ Single-celled foraminifera use calcium carbonate from seawater to build their skeletons, called tests. Much of the ocean floor, down to a depth of 4,000 m (about 13,000 ft), is covered with a thick ooze made up of tiny, accumulated calcite foraminifera tests and other planktonic shells.

▼ The chalk of England's famous White Cliffs of Dover is a sedimentary rock made from this calcareous seafloor ooze and then lifted above sea level.

that release oxygen into the shallow ocean water take in carbon dioxide from the water. Many types of sea animals, from microscopic foraminifera and nannoplankton to larger organisms such as barnacles, clams, and lobsters, use calcium carbonate derived from carbon dioxide to build their shells.

pH

Fresh water and seawater are solutions that have a **pH**. The pH scale measures the hydrogen ion concentration of a solution. Pure water has a pH of 7.0, which is neither acidic (pH less than 7.0) nor basic (pH greater than 7.0, also called alkaline).

Which do you think is more acidic: a drop of water from a pond or a raindrop? The raindrop, as it turns out, is often far more acidic than the pond water. In part, this is because dissolved carbon dioxide (CO_2) forms weak carbonic acid in the raindrop as it falls through the atmosphere. But the air also contains stronger acids that are picked up by the falling rain. Sulfuric acid can come from sulphate compounds released into the air by volcanoes or by humans burning fossil fuels. Nitric acid can come from fires, lightning, or again from humans burning fossil fuels.

Ocean surface water has an average pH of about 8.1, which makes it slightly basic. But slightly acidic rain falls on the ocean. And carbon dioxide dissolves into the water at the ocean's surface to form carbonic acid. So why is the water at the ocean's surface slightly basic instead of slightly acidic?

The ocean maintains its stable, slightly basic pH level because it has a chemical buffering system. A **buffer** is a substance that can either tie up or release hydrogen ions in order to maintain a solution's pH within a certain range.

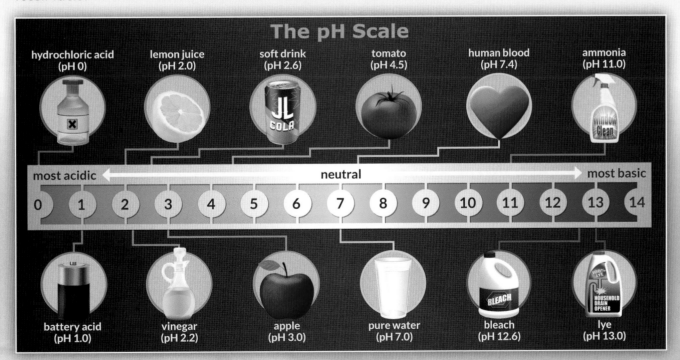

The pH Scale

hydrochloric acid (pH 0) | lemon juice (pH 2.0) | soft drink (pH 2.6) | tomato (pH 4.5) | human blood (pH 7.4) | ammonia (pH 11.0)

most acidic ← | neutral | → most basic

0 1 2 3 4 5 6 7 8 9 10 11 12 13 14

battery acid (pH 1.0) | vinegar (pH 2.2) | apple (pH 3.0) | pure water (pH 7.0) | bleach (pH 12.6) | lye (pH 13.0)

Rain falling in or downwind of urban areas that have heavy air pollution typically has a pH of around 5.0 and can locally be as low as 2.0. That's as acidic as lemon juice!

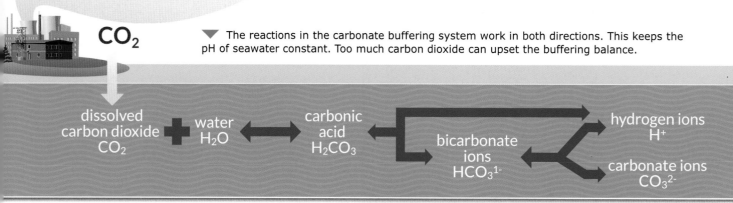

The reactions in the carbonate buffering system work in both directions. This keeps the pH of seawater constant. Too much carbon dioxide can upset the buffering balance.

dissolved carbon dioxide CO$_2$ **+** water H$_2$O ⟷ carbonic acid H$_2$CO$_3$ ⟷ bicarbonate ions HCO$_3^{1-}$ → hydrogen ions H$^+$ carbonate ions CO$_3^{2-}$

A chemical buffering system involves more than one chemical or more than one chemical reaction to achieve buffering.

If seawater starts to become too basic, carbonic acid in the water dissociates — that is, breaks apart into simpler molecules — to form bicarbonate ions and hydrogen ions. The added hydrogen ions lower the water's pH, reestablishing the proper pH level. The buffering system works in the opposite direction as well. If the seawater starts to become too acidic, bicarbonate ions will recombine with hydrogen ions to form carbonic acid. This removes hydrogen ions and raises the water's pH, making it less acidic.

The carbonate buffering system also allows the ocean to remove excess carbon dioxide from the atmosphere. The ocean has already absorbed about half the carbon dioxide released by humans burning fossil fuels. But too much carbon dioxide in Earth's atmosphere has led to increased carbon dioxide entering the seawater. The buffering system has become overloaded, and the ocean has started to gradually experience lower pH. We call this **ocean acidification**. Ocean acidification can harm many kinds of life in the ocean. For example, animals such as corals and clams have more difficulty making their calcium carbonate shells as the ocean becomes more acidic.

Density

Another important property of water is its density. **Density** is a measure of how much mass something has per unit volume. The density of pure water at 4°C (39°F) is 1.0 g/mL. Salt water's density is greater than 1.0 g/mL because the water contains additional dissolved salts. You would expect salt water to sink beneath fresh water because the salt water is denser.

The saltier and denser water is, the more buoyant objects are when placed in it. The same ship floats higher in seawater than in fresh water. And if you were to go for a swim in the Dead Sea

Fast Fact

Obviously you would not want to be in a ship sailing over an underwater volcano when the volcano erupted. If Kick'em Jenny, an underwater volcano located in the Caribbean Sea near Grenada, were to erupt the way it did in 1939, it could throw hot rocks several kilometers away. But an eruption might not be the only threat from Kick'em Jenny. In 1944, a wooden schooner disappeared near the volcano, leaving no wreckage and no sign of the 60 people on board. Kick'em Jenny had erupted the year before. Was it possible that the volcano was still actively releasing gases into the water in 1944? When submarine volcanoes release large quantities of gas bubbles into the water, it lowers the density of the water above. A ship sailing into an area of lower water density might suddenly lose its buoyancy — its ability to float — and sink. For this reason, ships are not supposed to sail within 1.5 km (1 mi) of Kick'em Jenny.

in Israel, you would find that you float higher in the salty water than anywhere else on Earth.

Water density is also affected by the water's temperature. Cold water is denser than warm water. Therefore, cold water should sink beneath warm water. Water temperature affects water density more than salinity. The densest water in the ocean is formed near Earth's poles where the air temperatures and ocean surface temperatures are coldest.

Check for Understanding

- How does a raindrop become acidic?
- Why does seawater become more acidic when buffering should maintain its normal pH?
- Compare the density of cold water and warm water.

Temperature

It should not surprise you that the warmest ocean water is found near the equator and the coldest water is found near Earth's poles. Water temperatures in the ocean vary with latitude. Seasons also affect water temperature, just as they affect air temperature. Over the course of a year at a given location, surface water is warmest in the summer and coldest in the winter.

The water at the ocean's surface is usually warmer than the water below. This is more obvious at lower latitudes, away from the poles and closer to Earth's equator. Sunlight warms the water at the ocean's surface. Wind and waves then help mix that warm surface water with cooler water just below, forming a zone of warmer water to a depth of a few hundred meters. This top layer, called the **mixed layer**, is the warmest layer of ocean water.

Beneath the mixed layer is a layer of water called the **thermocline**. The thermocline is a boundary layer separating the warm mixed layer from the very cold, deep, ocean layer beneath. It is most developed in the tropics, where the water is very warm at the surface and cold at the seafloor; it is absent entirely at the poles in the winter, where the water is well-mixed through the water column. Water temperature in the thermocline falls much more rapidly with depth than in the mixed layer or in the deep zone beneath the thermocline. About 90% of the ocean's total volume is found in the **deep water layer** beneath the thermocline.

Try This!

Take a room-temperature baby carrot and break off a small piece (about 1 cm). Add lukewarm water to a clear plastic cup until the cup is two-thirds full. Drop in the piece of carrot. What happens to the carrot? Now add a spoonful of table salt to the water. Stir to dissolve the salt. Keep adding salt until the carrot floats. How could you get the carrot to sink again or to hover in the middle of the water?

Salt water freezes at a slightly lower temperature than fresh water. Dissolved salts in the water lower the water's freezing point. This is why people spread salt on sidewalks and roads in the winter. The salt keeps the pavement ice-free at temperatures lower than fresh water's freezing point of 0°C (32°F). Seawater contains enough dissolved solids that it does not freeze except at very low temperatures. Even at Earth's poles, seawater only freezes at the ocean's surface where the air and water are coldest. Seawater of average salinity freezes at a temperature of about -2°C (28°F). At least 15% of the ocean is covered by sea ice at some point in the year.

Sunlight penetrates and warms the water of the **mixed layer**. The temperature of water in this zone is highly dependent on the latitude and season.

The temperature of water decreases rapidly in the thermocline. The depth and thickness of the **thermocline** varies with the latitude and season.

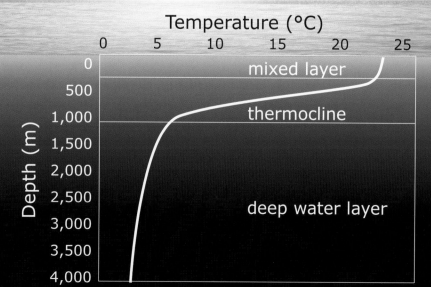

Ocean Depth vs. Temperature

Thermal Expansion

All matter tends to change its volume in response to a change in temperature. This is called **thermal expansion**. Most substances expand, or increase, their volume as their temperature increases. Most substances also contract, or decrease, their volume as they cool.

Water is unusual in that it actually expands when it freezes. You might know that from trying to freeze water in a closed container and having the container split open. If the same mass of water takes up 9% more volume when it freezes, what happens to the water's density? It decreases. This is why ice floats.

Water acts like other liquids at temperatures above freezing. Liquid fresh water contracts as it cools and reaches its minimum volume and maximum density at around 4°C (39°F).

Like most other materials, water expands as it warms. As Earth warms due to climate change, the temperature of water in the ocean slowly increases and its volume expands. This has implications for Earth's coastal communities and for rising sea level. As much as half of the observed increase in sea level is due to the ocean's water expanding as it becomes warmer. For every 1°C (1.8°F) increase in surface-water temperatures, sea level rises by 10 cm (4 in.). Over time, the deeper ocean water will also become warmer and expand, raising global sea level even more.

Heat Capacity

There's one other important property of water. **Specific heat** is the amount of thermal energy needed to raise the temperature of 1 g of a substance by 1°C. Water has a very high specific **heat capacity**. Compared with many other substances, it takes a lot of energy to raise the temperature of water. It may take the sun only a couple of hours to make a lake's sandy beach too hot to walk across barefoot. But it might take all summer for the sun to significantly raise the lake's water temperature.

And because of its high heat capacity, once water is warm, it takes a long time for it to cool down. Fish living at the bottom of a lake appreciate that in the middle of winter.

Water's ability to absorb and slowly release a great deal of thermal energy allows us to use water in an automobile radiator. The water cools the engine by absorbing large amounts of thermal energy without overheating. Some homes in colder climates also use water in their heating systems. Water transports thermal energy from the boiler to radiators in the house and back to the boiler.

Ocean water helps "even out" temperatures of coastal towns and states. Coastal areas are often warmer in the winter and cooler in the summer than locations farther inland, away from the water. Because of the ocean's size and the heat capacity of water versus the air in the atmosphere, it is estimated that over 93% of the excess heat due to global warming is being absorbed by the ocean.

Check for Understanding

- Compare the freezing point of fresh water and seawater.
- Describe how the volume of an ice cube changes as the ice slowly melts.

Lab 1.2

Properties of Water

The water quality of an area can affect the kinds of plants and animals that can live in the water. As Katy Croff Bell, Robert Ballard, and their Kolumbo Volcano exploration team know, it can also affect living things on shore. When Kolumbo erupted in 1650 AD, gases emitted from the underwater volcano killed many people and animals on Santorini, an island located only 7 km (4.3 mi) from the eruption. Today, the high rate of carbon dioxide emission into the water from the hydrothermal vents in Kolumbo has created a dense, acidic environment harmful to fish and other animals that normally live in and around underwater volcanoes. There are some living things, however, that thrive in the mineral-rich waters — bacteria! High concentrations of bacteria in Kolumbo's deep water lead to very high turbidity, making it difficult to see while exploring the volcano.

In this activity, you will explore various water properties. You will measure salinity, test pH, and check the level of dissolved oxygen in two mystery water samples.

Materials

- **mystery water sample "A"**
- **mystery water sample "B"**
- **cup or small beaker**
- **6 strips pH paper, 1–14 scale**
- **Lab 1.2 Data Sheet**
- **12 dissolved oxygen tablets**
- **10-mL test tube with cap**
- **hydrometer (see Build and Calibrate a Hydrometer, p. 31)**

Part 1: Test the pH Level

1. Gather two mystery water samples from your teacher. Carefully observe the two water samples and record any physical differences.

2. Pour a small amount of water sample A into a cup or small beaker.

3. Dip a pH strip into the water sample, and remove it immediately.

4. Watch the pH strip for a change in color. Match the color to the pH scale provided with the pH strips.

5. Repeat the test two more times, using a different pH strip each time. Record each result in the pH table on the Lab 1.2 Data Sheet.

6. Average your results, and record the average in the Data Summary table on the Lab 1.2 Data Sheet.

7. Repeat steps 2 to 6 for water sample B.

Part 2: Test the Dissolved Oxygen Level

1. Submerge a 10-mL test tube into water sample A. Cap the test tube before you remove it from the water.

2. Remove the test tube from the water and check for air bubbles. If you can see air bubbles, empty the test tube and start again.

3. Carefully remove the cap from the test tube and add two dissolved oxygen tablets. Note that some of the water will spill out.

4. Carefully replace the cap on the test tube, trying not to introduce air bubbles into the water.

5. Shake the test tube gently until the tablets have dissolved completely.

6. Watch the water for a change in color. Match the color to the color chart provided with the dissolved oxygen tablets.

7. Repeat the test two more times, and record each result in the Dissolved Oxygen table on the Lab 1.2 Data Sheet.

8. Average your results, and record the average in the Data Summary table on the Lab 1.2 Data Sheet.

9. Repeat steps 1 to 8 for water sample B.

Part 3: Test Salinity

1. Build and calibrate a hydrometer using the directions on the Build and Calibrate a Hydrometer sheet.

2. Place your hydrometer in water sample A.

3. Once the hydrometer settles, read the salinity level on the scale you created. If the level is between two lines, estimate the salinity.

4. Repeat the test two more times and record each result in the Salinity table on the Lab 1.2 Data Sheet.

5. Average your results, and record the average in the Data Summary table on the Lab 1.2 Data Sheet.

6. Repeat steps 2 to 5 for water sample B.

Reflect and Apply

1. Use the data you recorded in the Data Summary table on the Lab 1.2 Data Sheet to create bar graphs showing the chemical properties of each sample.

2. Compare the chemical properties of the two water samples. Which properties are similar for each sample? Which are different? Where might you expect to find each sample?

Extension

Collect water from several places in your local area. For example, collect tap water, rain water, and water from a creek. Perform the same tests that you performed on the water samples in this lab. Graph the results. Which chemical properties are the same among the samples? Which are different?

Journal Question

How are the chemical properties of water important, and why is it important for scientists to monitor changes in these properties?

▶ *Hercules* uses a gas-tight container to capture hot fluids bubbling from a hydrothermal vent.

◀ *Hercules's* manipulator arm carefully grasps a sample of a hydrothermal vent "chimney."

Build and Calibrate a Hydrometer

A hydrometer is a tool used to measure the salinity of water. Follow the directions below to build and calibrate a hydrometer.

Materials

- empty 2-L bottle with the top cut off or other tall, clear container
- 1 L distilled water at room temperature
- 90 g (3.2 oz) salt
- ballpoint pen with a white or clear barrel
- 150 g (5 oz) water-proof modeling clay
- fine-tip permanent marker
- towel

1. Remove the ink stick from a ballpoint pen. Do not replace the cap on the pen.

2. Use a fine-tip permanent marker to mark a line about 5 cm (2 in.) from the top end of the pen barrel. Write "salinity (ppt)" above the line. Label the line 0. Parts per thousand (ppt) indicates how many parts of salt there are per thousand parts of water.

3. Place a small ball of modeling clay around the other end of the pen barrel. This is your hydrometer.

4. Slowly place the hydrometer with the clay side facing down in a container filled with 1 L distilled water.

5. Once the pen barrel has settled, check the location of the 0 line you marked on the barrel. Add or remove clay until the line is exactly at the level of the top of the water. Your hydrometer now reads 0 salinity ppt in distilled water, which is accurate.

6. Remove the hydrometer from the water and dry it off.

7. Measure 30 g salt (1.06 oz). Stir the salt into the distilled water. Be sure to stir until the salt is completely dissolved.

8. Return the hydrometer to the water. Once it settles, carefully mark a line at the new water level. Label this line "30" since your water now has a salinity of 30 ppt.

9. Repeat steps 7 and 8 two more times. Label the new lines "60" and "90." Your hydrometer is now calibrated from 0 to 90 ppt.

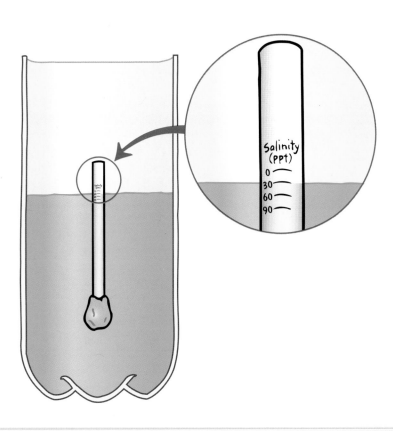

Dawn Wright

Career: Marine Geographer and Geologist
Born: Baltimore, MD
Education: B.A., Wheaton College, Wheaton, IL
Ph.D., University of California, Santa Barbara

Dawn Wright's early research focused on the fissures, or cracks, in the seafloor near mid-ocean ridges. These fissures are where magma comes up near the seafloor and where water circulates down into the cracks, gets heated, and resurfaces at hydrothermal vents. It was this interest that led to Wright's 1991 dive aboard the *Alvin*, the three-person submersible famous for its 1986 dive exploring the wreck of the *Titanic*. In the 8-hour dive to an area near the East Pacific Rise, Wright was able to observe and photograph the fissures firsthand.

Wright's 1991 dive was historic in that she was the first African-American woman to dive in the *Alvin*. "The number of women in ocean sciences is still very low, especially for minorities. I want minority students to think about marine science as a possibility. And even if you are the only woman or the only person of color in the room, it doesn't have to defeat you. Just enjoy what you do, and do it in the best way that you can!"

Wright's other interest is geography. She is a leading authority on geographic information systems (GIS), which can be used to display and analyze data in ways that allow the data to be better studied and interpreted. Wright is now serving as Chief Scientist of Esri, a company that develops GIS software and promotes the use of GIS in classrooms and research labs worldwide. She is also an affiliate professor of geography and oceanography at Oregon State University.

Wright with the submersible *Pisces* before a dive in American Samoa in 2005

Q & A

Were you always interested in oceanography?
Not always, but close. When I was young, I watched the astronauts walking on the moon and wanted to be an astronaut. But by the time I was eight, I had pretty much decided to become an oceanographer.

What got you interested in the ocean?
I was always reading books about the sea — *Mutiny on the Bounty, Treasure Island*, anything with a sea adventure. And then there was Jacques Cousteau. My generation grew up with Jacques Cousteau television specials. They had a tremendous impact on me.

What about your interest in geology?
I got interested in geology — rocks and volcanoes, in particular — in high school. I decided then to put myself on the path that led to geological oceanography.

Do you have any advice for students interested in getting into a STEM career?
Even if math isn't your strongest subject, it's a good idea to stick with it and do the best you can. Get as much experience as you can on computers. Do research on the career you're interested in. The more personal research you do, the better. Finally, have a balance of other interests. Keeping yourself a well-rounded person is a good recipe for success.

In This Stage:

Your expedition goal is accomplished when you:

Can describe what causes a density current.

Know how the global ocean conveyor works to redistribute heat.

Why this is important:

Understanding the global ocean conveyor is critical to understanding the importance of the ocean in maintaining Earth's climate.

Words to identify:

current, density current, deep-ocean current, thermohaline current, global ocean conveyor

Stage 3: In the Loop

Deep-Ocean Currents

There are two main types of ocean currents: surface currents and deep-ocean currents. A **current** is a large stream of moving water that moves within a larger body of water. Surface currents are driven mainly by winds blowing across the ocean surface. Surface currents move water down to a depth of only about 100 to 200 m (330 to 660 ft).

As the name implies, deep-ocean currents move through much deeper water than surface currents. Deep-ocean currents are density currents. A **density current** is a current caused by gravity acting on two fluids of different densities. A density current occurs in the ocean when water of a greater density sinks beneath water of a lesser density.

Thermohaline Currents

Katy Croff Bell sees **deep-ocean currents** at work in her expeditions on E/V *Nautilus*. These deep-ocean currents are caused by thermohaline circulation. According to Bell, "The word 'thermohaline' is actually a combination of two words — *thermo* meaning "temperature" and *haline* meaning "salt." So when you have water with different

combinations of coldness and saltiness, the water starts to move and the result is thermohaline circulation." Remember that both temperature and salinity affect the density of water. The colder and saltier the water becomes, the denser it becomes. A **thermohaline current** is a density current caused by water masses with different temperatures and/or salinities.

Not surprisingly, Earth's deep-ocean currents begin at high latitudes near the poles. Because of the way the sun's energy hits our spherical planet, air temperature is higher at the equator and lower at the poles. It follows that, wherever very cold air is in contact with the water, the water at the ocean's surface can become very cold and dense. This cold, salty water sinks because it has a greater density than the layer of water beneath it.

Eventually the sinking, dense water encounters something that changes its movement from vertical to horizontal. The water starts slowly moving sideways as a deep-ocean current. Some deep-ocean currents creep along the ocean floor. Others move along at other depths, slowly sliding over water of even greater density. The deep-ocean currents are deflected by Earth's rotation and by the continental margins.

Check for Understanding
- Describe how a density current works.
- Why do deep-ocean currents start at high latitudes?

The Global Ocean Conveyor

The deep-ocean currents are connected with surface currents in a pattern sometimes referred to as the **global ocean conveyor** because it acts like a conveyor belt. What does a conveyor belt do? A conveyor belt transports something from one place to another. Think about going through the checkout line at a grocery. You place your groceries on the conveyor belt and they move from the far end toward the cashier. The belt forms a continuous loop; it comes up at the far end, carries the groceries along, disappears at the cashier's end, and then wraps back around underneath. Conveyor belts are used to carry groceries, packages, luggage, coal, and other items from one place to another.

Try This!

Make colored ice cubes using water and food coloring. Add uncolored room-temperature water to a long, flat, clear container such as a glass baking pan or lasagna dish. Now add a colored ice cube to one end of the container. What happens to the colored water as the ice cube melts?

Global Ocean Conveyor Circulation

In this diagram of Earth's thermohaline circulation, cold, high-density water forms near the poles. Find the water that descends near Greenland and becomes the North Atlantic Deep Water current. Follow the circulation of the water as it enters different ocean basins and ascends to join warm-water surface currents, eventually returning to the North Atlantic.

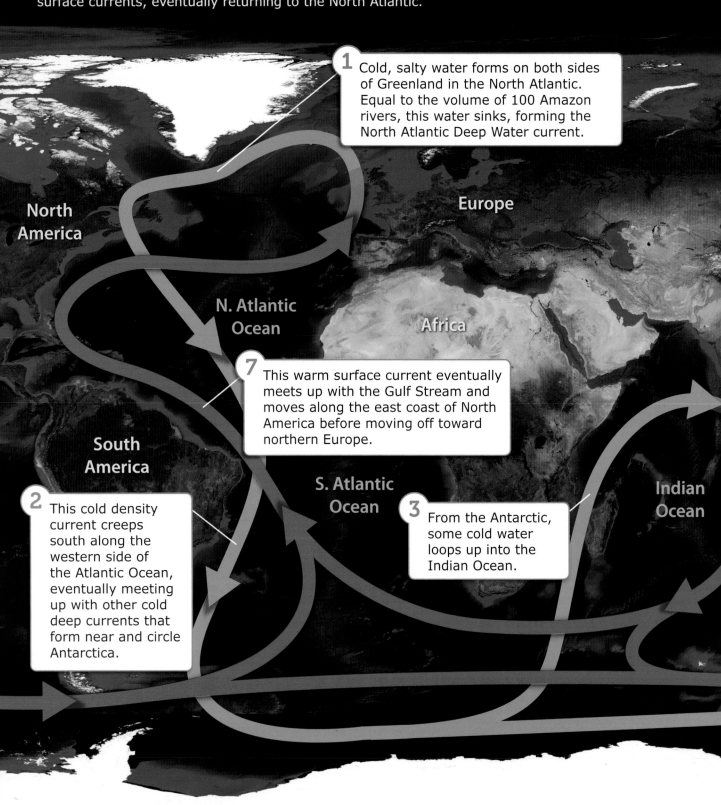

North America

Europe

1 Cold, salty water forms on both sides of Greenland in the North Atlantic. Equal to the volume of 100 Amazon rivers, this water sinks, forming the North Atlantic Deep Water current.

N. Atlantic Ocean

Africa

7 This warm surface current eventually meets up with the Gulf Stream and moves along the east coast of North America before moving off toward northern Europe.

South America

S. Atlantic Ocean

Indian Ocean

2 This cold density current creeps south along the western side of the Atlantic Ocean, eventually meeting up with other cold deep currents that form near and circle Antarctica.

3 From the Antarctic, some cold water loops up into the Indian Ocean.

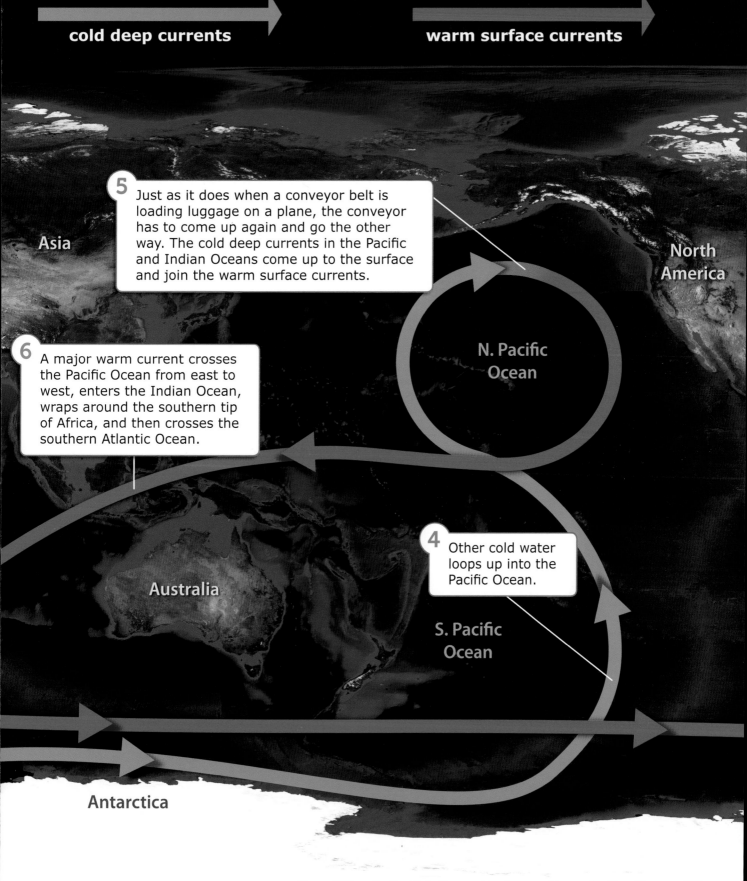

cold deep currents

warm surface currents

5 Just as it does when a conveyor belt is loading luggage on a plane, the conveyor has to come up again and go the other way. The cold deep currents in the Pacific and Indian Oceans come up to the surface and join the warm surface currents.

Asia

North America

N. Pacific Ocean

6 A major warm current crosses the Pacific Ocean from east to west, enters the Indian Ocean, wraps around the southern tip of Africa, and then crosses the southern Atlantic Ocean.

4 Other cold water loops up into the Pacific Ocean.

Australia

S. Pacific Ocean

Antarctica

Aside from water (which is the belt itself), what do you think the global ocean conveyor is carrying from one place to another? The most important thing transported by the global ocean conveyor is thermal energy. This system of surface and deep-ocean currents helps redistribute thermal energy on Earth. Warm surface water flows from the tropics toward the poles. The warm water heats the air above, forming air masses that moderate the climate. Without the circulation of warm water toward the poles, temperatures at the higher latitudes would be much colder than they are now.

The cold, salty water masses that form and sink in the North Atlantic near Greenland and Iceland and in the Southern Ocean near Antarctica contain high concentrations of dissolved oxygen. While nutrients can sink through the water column and reach organisms in the deep ocean, it takes the deep currents to deliver and distribute dissolved oxygen needed for marine life living in deeper water. The overturning of water by the global conveyor brings oxygen down from the ocean's surface.

Circulation in the Atlantic Ocean is probably the most important part of the global ocean conveyor. In the Atlantic, there are no land masses preventing circulation from one pole to the other.

If you could tag a water molecule on the day it sinks as part of the North Atlantic Deep Water current, it might take 1,000 years for that molecule to return to coastal Greenland. This is an enormous — and complicated — conveyor belt.

Changes in the Global Conveyor

The global ocean conveyor has not always worked the way it does now. Millions of years ago, Earth's tectonic plates were not located where they are today. The continents were in different positions and locations. The deep currents we know today did not exist. Antarctica separated from South America around 34 million

years ago, allowing for the formation of the Antarctic Circumpolar Current that cut Antarctica off from warm water and plunged it into a deep freeze. Then, around 5 million years ago, North America and South America became joined by the Isthmus of Panama, cutting off the flow of warm, tropical water from the Atlantic Ocean to the Pacific Ocean. Since that time, the global ocean conveyor has worked pretty much the way we see it now.

However, there was one time when the conveyor shut down. Around 13,000 years ago, Earth's last ice age was ending. Glaciers were retreating and fresh meltwater was pouring into the oceans. In central Canada, a huge freshwater lake had formed out in front of the retreating ice sheet. Eventually, the lake broke through an ice dam and quickly drained out into the Arctic Ocean through what we now call the Hudson Bay. Some scientists believe that this sudden massive addition of fresh water made its way to the North Atlantic where it shut down the conveyor belt by decreasing the density of the water in the North Atlantic. The normally cold, salty water no longer sank. The global ocean conveyor slowed and stopped. Without the conveyor bringing warm water to the poles, temperatures declined in the Northern Hemisphere, particularly at higher latitudes. Glaciers temporarily advanced again. This mini-ice age, called the Younger Dryas, lasted 1,300 years.

Check for Understanding

- How is the global ocean conveyor like a conveyor belt?
- Briefly describe how the global ocean conveyor redistributes thermal energy on Earth.

Technology Connection

Argo Floats

Scientists maintain approximately 3,500 free-drifting, data collection floats as part of the Argo program. Argo floats do not just gather data at the ocean's surface. Instead, each float descends to a depth of 1,000 m (3,300 ft) and drifts for nine days. On the tenth day, the float descends to 2,000 m (6,600 ft) and then gathers temperature and salinity data as it ascends back to the ocean surface. Satellites determine the position of the floats when they surface and receive temperature and salinity data transmitted by the floats.

Weight: There are different models of Argo floats. The average weight is about 40 kg (88 lb).

Diving: The float has a bladder at the bottom and a pump that can fill the bladder with oil or pump the oil out of the bladder. Changes in the bladder allow the float to sink and resurface.

Lifespan: The Argo floats are normally able to function as long as their batteries are strong enough to pump the float back up to the ocean surface. The average lifespan is four years.

Data from Argo floats show that water temperatures in the upper 2,000 m (6,600 ft) of the ocean are increasing. The warming of the upper ocean concerns climate scientists.

Layers of Water

It is no accident that Katy Croff Bell and the Corps of Exploration on E/V *Nautilus* have discovered dozens of ancient shipwrecks in the Black Sea. They chose that area to explore based on their understanding of density and their knowledge of the physical features of the seafloor. The preservation of shipwrecks in the deep waters of the Black Sea is made possible because of differences in the density of fresh water and salt water. All bodies of water have a less dense layer of water over a denser layer. In most places, these layers mix. The unique conditions in the Black Sea, however, prevent the layers from mixing, keeping oxygen in the shallower waters from reaching the deeper waters. This layering means that wrecks found in the deepest waters of the Black Sea are well preserved, while wrecks in the shallower waters are not.

In this activity, you will explore how temperature and salinity affect the density of water. You will combine water with different properties and observe the layering that occurs.

Materials

- clear plastic container about the size of a shoe box
- wooden block, book, or other object for propping up one end of the container
- 830 mL (3.5 c) room-temperature water
- 60 mL (0.25 c) hot water
- 60 mL (0.25 c) ice water
- 15 mL (1 Tbsp) salt
- 3 small beakers or cups
- measuring cup
- plastic spoon or stirring rod
- red, green, and blue food coloring
- Lab 1.3 Data Sheet
- colored pencils

pour slowly

Part 1: Prepare the Solutions

1. Place a wooden block, book, or other object under one end of the plastic container. Add about 770 mL (3.25 c) room-temperature water to the container.

2. Mix 60 mL (0.25 c) hot water and one drop of red food coloring in a cup. Label the cup "hot."

3. Mix 60 mL (0.25 c) room-temperature water, 15 mL (1 Tbsp) salt, and one drop of green food coloring in a cup. Label the cup "salty."

4. Mix 60 mL (0.25 c) ice water and one drop of blue food coloring in a cup. Label the cup "cold."

Part 2: Create Density Layers

1. On the Lab 1.3 Data Sheet, make a prediction about what will happen when you add each of the colored solutions to the room-temperature water in the container.

2. Slowly pour the red solution into the container. For best results, hold the cup with the solution as close to the container as possible, and slowly pour the solution onto the exposed bottom of the raised end of the container.

3. Observe the container from the side at eye level. Record your observations on the Lab 1.3 Data Sheet.

4. Repeat steps 2 and 3 for the green and blue solutions.

Reflect and Apply

1. Describe the characteristics of the three colored solutions.

2. Why did the different solutions separate into layers?

3. Describe a solution that you think would layer between the green and blue layers.

Extension

Create a mixture of water, salt, and yellow food coloring that will form a layer underneath the blue layer. Add your mixture to the container and observe what happens. If your mixture does not fall in the correct place, adjust it and try again.

Journal Question

How do the salinity and temperature of water affect whether an object floats or sinks in it?

STEM Spotlight

Claudia Benitez-Nelson

Career: Chemical Oceanographer
Born: Waterbury, CT
Education: B.S., University of Washington
                    Ph.D., Woods Hole Oceanographic Institution

Claudia Benitez-Nelson began her life on the East Coast, but grew up in Seattle. "Seattle is a very environmentally conscious city. I couldn't help but be aware of environmental issues." So with an interest in both chemistry and oceanography, it is not surprising that some of her early work had to do with global climate change and Earth's ocean. Benitez-Nelson studied how carbon dioxide is removed from the atmosphere by the formation and sinking of carbon-containing particles in the ocean.

Today, Benitez-Nelson is both a researcher and a teacher. She is a professor at the University of South Carolina and Director of the Marine Science Program. "I love teaching and having students in my lab. They ask fabulous questions, sometimes odd questions that I should know the answers to but don't. And that makes me think. It brings me back to basics. Why haven't I thought about that aspect of my work in awhile? Those questions have even pushed my research in new directions. I love it!"

When Benitez-Nelson is not mentoring her undergraduate students or local public school kids, she continues to pursue her research interests. "I examine water nutrient level cycles. Those affect algal blooms, which produce harmful toxins that have direct impacts on fisheries and beach quality."

Benitez-Nelson programming a submersible pump to collect water column samples

Q & A

Why did you agree to be featured as a STEM Spotlight?
Being a person of color myself and seeing so few people of color in science, I want students to know that we are out there and available to them. I did this. You can do this, too.

Did you always want to be an oceanographer?
No. I have always been interested in science. Between kindergarten and the start of college, I wanted to be everything from an astronaut to a forest ranger. I took an introductory oceanography course early in college and I really liked it. And even better, I found a way to combine it with chemistry, which I was good at.

What advice would you give a student interested in pursuing a career in oceanography?
If you think oceanography is something that you would really like to do, then do it! Remember, you can look for help or advice. I guarantee you will find someone out there who will be happy to guide you. It's a great job. There are opportunities to travel and meet people from all over the world. And you get to do research on things that you find interesting.

Do you have any general advice for students?
You can do anything that you set your mind to. What is important is that you be willing to try — even if you think something is too hard or too difficult. Take that risk!

Monitoring Changes in Water

Recall that your expedition goal is to understand the nature and importance of Earth's ocean. Now that you have been fully briefed, you will apply your understanding of the properties of ocean water to explore a local water source. Understanding our local water sources is important because, though we do not all live near an ocean, we are all connected to the ocean through our watersheds. A watershed is an area of land in which all water drains to a common outlet, such as a stream, a river, or the ocean. Small watersheds drain into bigger ones. Eventually, most watersheds drain into the ocean.

In this field assignment, you will trace your local watershed back to the ocean to see how it is connected. You will then investigate the properties of water at a local water source and develop a plan to monitor the source for changes over time. As you do this, you will build an understanding of how your local environment relates to environments around the world, the ocean, and climate.

Expedition Challenge

- Identify your local watershed and trace it back to the ocean.
- Conduct a field study of water properties at a local water source.
- Develop a plan for monitoring changes to the water at a local water source.

Materials
- **Expedition 1 Field Assignment Data Sheet**
- **hydrometer (see Build and Calibrate a Hydrometer, p. 31)**
- **Secchi disk (see Build a Secchi Disk, p. 43)**
- **field notebook**
- **bucket**
- **3 strips pH paper, 1–14 scale**
- **6 dissolved oxygen tablets**
- **10-mL test tube with cap**
- **thermometer**
- **blue clothespin**
- **red clothespin**
- **2 field marker flags, cones, or other markers**
- **measuring tape**
- **3 oranges**
- **stopwatch**
- **optional: camera**

Field Prep

1. Your teacher will provide you with the name of a local water source and a specific area for your field study. Examine a topographic contour map that shows the area. What is the terrain like near the water source?

2. Look at a watershed map. Identify your local watershed, and note where your watershed drains into the ocean.

3. Explore an online physical map of your region. Locate the body of water where you will do your field study. Zoom out to follow that body of water. Where does it drain? Trace the path of the water from your watershed to the ocean. At what point does the path meet the ocean?

4. To prepare for your field study, gather your materials and, if necessary, build a Secchi disk and a hydrometer.

Part 1: Assess and Document the Field Study Site

1. When you arrive at the field study site, record a brief description of the site in your field notebook. Sketch the site and mark its location on the topographic map. If possible, photograph the site.

2. Select two locations within the field study site to take water samples. Try to select locations that differ in at least one way such as in the depth of the water, choppiness of the water, type of vegetation present, or amount of shade. Mark the locations as "Location A" and "Location B" on your sketch of the field site, and record a detailed description of each location. If possible, photograph each of the locations.

Part 2: Test the Salinity at Location A

1. Collect at least 1 L (4 c) water from Location A in a bucket.
2. Place the hydrometer in the bucket of water.
3. Once the hydrometer settles, read the salinity level. If the level is between two lines, estimate the salinity.
4. Repeat the test two more times and record each result in the Salinity table on the Expedition 1 Field Assignment Data Sheet.
5. Average your results and record the average in the Data Summary table.

Part 3: Test the pH Level at Location A

1. Dip a pH strip into the water (either in the bucket of collected water or directly from the water source) and remove it immediately.
2. Watch the pH strip for a change in color. Match the color to the pH scale provided with the pH strips.
3. Repeat the test two more times, using a different pH strip each time. Record each result in the pH table on the Expedition 1 Field Assignment Data Sheet.
4. Average your results and record the average in the Data Summary table.

Part 4: Test the Dissolved Oxygen Level at Location A

1. Submerge a 10-mL test tube into the water. Cap the test tube before you remove it from the water.
2. Remove the test tube from the water and check for air bubbles. If you can see air bubbles, empty the test tube and start again.
3. Carefully remove the cap from the test tube and add two dissolved oxygen tablets. Note that some of the water will spill out.
4. Carefully replace the cap on the test tube, trying not to introduce air bubbles into the water.
5. Shake the test tube gently until the tablets dissolve completely.
6. Watch the water for a change in color. Match the color to the color chart provided with the dissolved oxygen tablets.

7. Repeat the test two more times and record each result in the Dissolved Oxygen table on the Expedition 1 Field Assignment Data Sheet.
8. Average your results and record the average in the Data Summary table.

Part 5: Measure the Water Temperature at Location A

1. Place the tip of the thermometer about 10 cm (4 in.) into the water and hold it there for 30 seconds.
2. Read the water temperature and record it in the Water Temperature table on the Expedition 1 Field Assignment Data Sheet.
3. Take the measurement two more times and record each result in the Water Temperature table.
4. Average your results and record the average in the Data Summary table.

Part 6: Test the Turbidity at Location A

1. Slowly lower the Secchi disk into the water at your chosen location until it is no longer visible. The Secchi disk should be lowered in shade. If no natural shade exists, lower the disk in shade from your body.
2. As soon as the Secchi disk is no longer visible, place a red clothespin on the rope at the water's surface. This clothespin marks the lowering depth.
3. Slowly raise the Secchi disk until the black and white pattern is just visible. Place a blue clothespin on the rope at the water's surface. This clothespin marks the rising depth.
4. Measure the distance from each clothespin to the disk to determine the lowering depth and rising depth. Record the depths in the Turbidity table on the Expedition 1 Field Assignment Data Sheet.
5. Average the lowering depth and rising depth to get the average depth, and record this in the Turbidity table
6. Repeat steps 1 to 5 two more times, and record all the results in the Turbidity table.
7. Average the three average depths, and record this average in the Data Summary table.

Part 7: Measure the Current Speed at Location A

1. Use a small flag or other marker to mark a spot near the edge of the water at your selected location. Call this "Point A."

2. Measure 12 m (40 ft) downstream from Point A and mark it with a flag. Call this "Point B."

3. Place one person at Point A and another person at Point B.

4. Place a person with an orange a few meters upstream of Point A.

5. Place a timekeeper with a stopwatch between Point A and Point B, and make sure that he or she can hear the people at both points.

6. The person with the orange should drop the orange into the current so that it floats past Points A and B.

7. When the orange passes Point A, the person at Point A should call out "start," and the timekeeper should start the stopwatch.

8. When the orange passes Point B, the person at Point B should call out "stop," and the timekeeper should stop the stopwatch.

9. Record the time it takes the orange to travel 12 m (40 ft) in the Current Speed table on the Expedition 1 Field Assignment Data Sheet.

10. Repeat steps 6 to 9 two more times.

11. Calculate the speed at which the orange traveled in the current for each trial by dividing the distance the orange traveled by the time it took to go that distance:

    speed = distance/time

12. Record the speed in meters per second (m/s) for each trial in the Current Speed table.

13. Calculate the average speed for all the trials, and record this average in the Data Summary table.

Part 8: Collect Data from Location B

1. Repeat the tests in Parts 2 through 7 at Location B.

How can you measure the depth of the water at your field site?

Design a tool to measure the water depth at your field study site. Make a list of materials you will need, or come up with a way to use the materials your teacher provides. Write a plan for how you will use the tool to measure depth. Have your teacher approve the tool and the plan. Create your tool and use it at your field site to collect and record water depth data.

Expedition Debrief

1. Return to your classroom and compile a report about the field site. Include descriptions, maps or sketches, and photographs (if available). Include the raw data you collected for both locations within the field study site, as well as an analysis of the data and the similarities and differences between the two locations. Create graphs and/or diagrams to visually communicate the similarities and differences at the two locations. What differences do you notice between Location A and Location B? What might explain these differences?

2. Go online to the Citizen Science section of the JASON website to report your findings and see what others have found in their locations.

3. Develop a strategy for monitoring changes to the water source at your field site over time. What data should be collected? How often should data be collected? What might you learn by monitoring the same site over time?

Journal Question

What information can the physical features and chemical properties of a water source tell us about the area? How could the condition of a local water source impact the ocean?

Build a Secchi Disk

Materials

- old CD
- ruler
- permanent marker with waterproof ink
- black duct tape
- white duct tape
- scissors
- 10 m (33 ft) nylon rope or kite string
- meter stick
- eye bolt with 3 nuts
- flat washers

1. Use a ruler and marker to divide the CD into four equal pie pieces.

2. Cover two pie pieces with black duct tape and two with white duct tape so that they alternate colors. Do not cover the hole in the middle of the CD.

3. Screw a nut onto the eye bolt, leaving about 4 cm (1.5 in.) of the bolt thread exposed. Stack a washer, then the CD (with the black and white part facing the eye of the bolt), and then another washer on the bolt. Screw the second nut onto the eye bolt. Tighten the two nuts to secure the CD between them.

4. Securely tie the rope to the eye of the bolt.

5. With the zero end of a meter stick resting on the CD, measure 1 m (3.3 ft) up the length of the rope, and use the marker to make a tick mark on the rope. Use the meter stick and marker to measure and mark additional 1-m tick marks along the entire length of the rope.

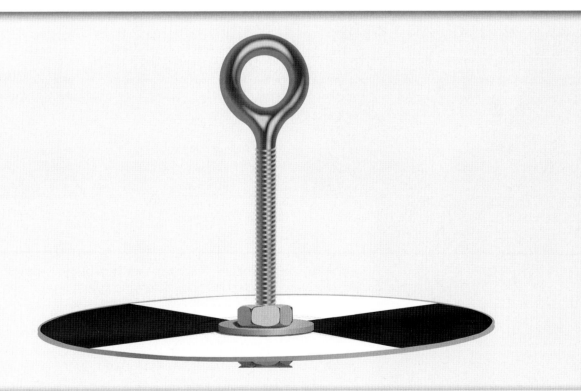

Expedition 2

Climate Connections
Drift and Flow

"Earth's climate connects us and affects us every day. It is critically important that we improve our understanding of how climate works and changes so we can make more informed decisions about our actions."

—Dr. Diane Stanitski
Program Manager
NOAA Office of Climate Observation

Diane Stanitski

Diane Stanitski's job at NOAA focuses on getting as many data-gathering instruments, such as drifting buoys, into the ocean as necessary to answer key scientific questions about climate. The data gathered help Stanitski and other scientists understand more about the ocean and its effect on climate.

Meet the Researcher Video
Come meet Diane Stanitski and John Adler, a pair of married climate scientists who travel the world, exploring unique environments and gathering critical data to better understand how Earth's climate is changing.

Read more about Stanitski and Adler on the JASON website.

Your Expedition Goal...

Investigate how energy flow in the Earth system creates global winds and surface currents, and influences climate.

To accomplish your goal successfully, you will need to:

- Describe how the sun's energy is transferred and balanced as part of Earth's energy budget.
- Discuss how Earth's natural greenhouse effect works and explain its significance to life on the planet.
- Explore how the unequal heating of Earth's surface and Earth's rotation result in patterns of global winds and ocean surface currents.
- Distinguish weather from climate.
- Identify Earth's major climate zones and explain how they are determined by latitude, sun angle, elevation, topography, cloud cover, and proximity to the ocean.
- Discuss natural factors that modify or control climate, such as the effects of clouds, ocean, and land.

Join the Team

The Argonaut team takes a break from their work on the R/V *Shearwater*. (L to R): Diane Stanitski, Sarah Mullins, John Adler, Marcelo Ancira, Keiana Yasunaka, and Lisa Conselatore.

Drifting with Argonauts

"We're going to go on the count of three. One... two... three!"

At first, JASON Argonaut Sarah Mullins thought the buoy might actually be too heavy to toss over the ship's rail. But together, she and fellow Argonaut Lisa Conselatore were able to throw the buoy into the waters off the California coast near the Channel Islands. The buoy was deployed!

When Diane Stanitski, John Adler, and the JASON Argonauts tossed the two Adopt a Drifter buoys off the side of the R/V *Shearwater* in July 2010, there was no way to know for sure where the ocean would carry the two instruments. One buoy was released in the Santa Barbara Channel and was expected to drift in local eddies before making its way to the Pacific. The other buoy was deployed beyond the Channel Islands and was expected to drift south. Beyond that, both buoys were at the mercy of the ocean's surface currents. After deployment, the buoys measured average ocean temperatures every 90 seconds and made the data available every hour.

As the Argonauts found out, sometimes gathering real-time data means encountering the unexpected. Instrument sensors can fail. Battery packs can go dead. In the case of the first drifting buoy launched by the Argos north of the Channel Islands, the drifter never made it to the open ocean. It was supposed to follow an eddy northwest along the California coast, pass Point Conception, and then continue west into the Pacific. It almost made it. Instead, the buoy washed up onshore and was salvaged by National Marine Sanctuaries staff.

The second drifting buoy adopted by the JASON team and deployed south of the Channel Islands did much better. After traveling south along the coast and circling in an eddy, the buoy moved west into the Pacific Ocean. The drifter sent back data for over a year and had almost made it to Hawai'i when its battery finally failed.

Expedition 1 Briefing Video

Prepare for your expedition by viewing this video clip. Learn how scientists such as Diane Stanitski and John Adler use different technologies to gather climate data from Earth's oceans.

In This Stage:

Your expedition goal is accomplished when you:

Know how the sun's energy reaches Earth.

Can describe how thermal energy is transferred and balanced as part of Earth's energy budget.

Understand Earth's "natural" greenhouse effect.

Why this is important:

The Earth system is balanced with incoming solar energy offset by energy lost to space. Knowing how Earth's energy budget might be altered is a key to understanding climate change.

Words to identify:

radiation, conduction, convection, energy budget, greenhouse effect

Stage 1: Energy from the Sun

Almost all of the energy that drives Earth's weather and climate comes from the sun, some 150 million km (93 million mi) away. Latitude, seasons, topography, and changing cloud cover affect the amount of sunlight falling on a given location, causing unequal heating of Earth's surface. Landforms, bodies of water, vegetation, buildings, roads, and other surfaces influence the amount and rate of energy absorption and transfer. Weather and climate are both affected by the way thermal energy — heat — flows through Earth's atmosphere and ocean.

Heat Transfer

Heat does not stay in the same place. It flows from warmer to cooler locations. Heat can be transferred in three ways: radiation, conduction, and convection.

When heat flows from a warmer place to a colder place, the colder place gains thermal energy. It heats up. If enough time is allowed to pass and there are no other external influences, the two places will eventually reach the same temperature and heat will stop flowing.

Types of Heat Transfer

Radiation

Radiation is the direct transfer of energy by electromagnetic waves. The flow of energy from the sun to Earth is an example of radiation. The light you see and the heat you feel when the sun falls on your face at noon are examples of energy moving from one place to another via radiation.

Conduction

Conduction occurs when heat is transferred between materials that are in direct contact. If you have ever accidentally touched a hot frying pan or walked barefoot on a hot sandy beach, you experienced heat transfer by conduction. Heat energy was conducted from the pan to your hand or from the sand to your foot.

Convection

In fluid materials, such as liquids and gases, heat can be transferred by the movement of the material itself. In general, warmer fluids are less dense than colder fluids. Therefore, warmer fluids tend to rise up through cooler fluids. Cooler, denser fluids sink through warmer fluids. This form of heat movement is called **convection**.

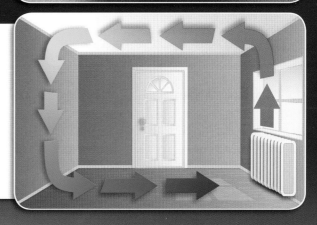

Sunlight and Earth

Solar radiation — energy from the sun — can change types when it enters the Earth system. Let's look at sunlight, for example. What happens when visible solar radiation — light — hits Earth's surface? Some of the visible light is reflected. Reflected visible light is what your eyes see and what allows you to see objects in your environment. But some of that visible light is absorbed by the materials of Earth's surface such as rocks, soil, plants, and water.

When solar radiation is absorbed by an object on the ground, the object heats up. But then it begins to release that thermal energy back into the surrounding environment. Some of the heat is conducted into nearby materials directly touching the object, including the air above. Other heat radiates back into the air as long-wave radiation, which also heats the air. The heated air begins to rise, transferring energy by convection. This transfer of heat from Earth's surface to the air energizes the atmosphere, driving the water cycle, creating winds, and producing our planet's weather.

Another 30% of the sunlight reaching Earth is reflected back into space by the atmosphere, clouds, or Earth's surface.

30% total reflected out

100% incoming shortwave solar radiation

reflected · reflected backscatter by clouds by surface

23% absorbed by clouds, H_2O, O_3, and dust

Clouds, molecules in the air, and particles (for example, dust or aerosols) absorb about 23% of the sunlight that reaches Earth's atmosphere.

47% absorbed by ocean and land

The remaining 47% of the sunlight that reaches Earth's surface is absorbed by Earth's ocean and by the land. Some of the visible light energy is converted into thermal energy — heat.

In a balanced energy budget, the remaining 70% of solar energy that enters Earth's atmosphere eventually leaves it again.

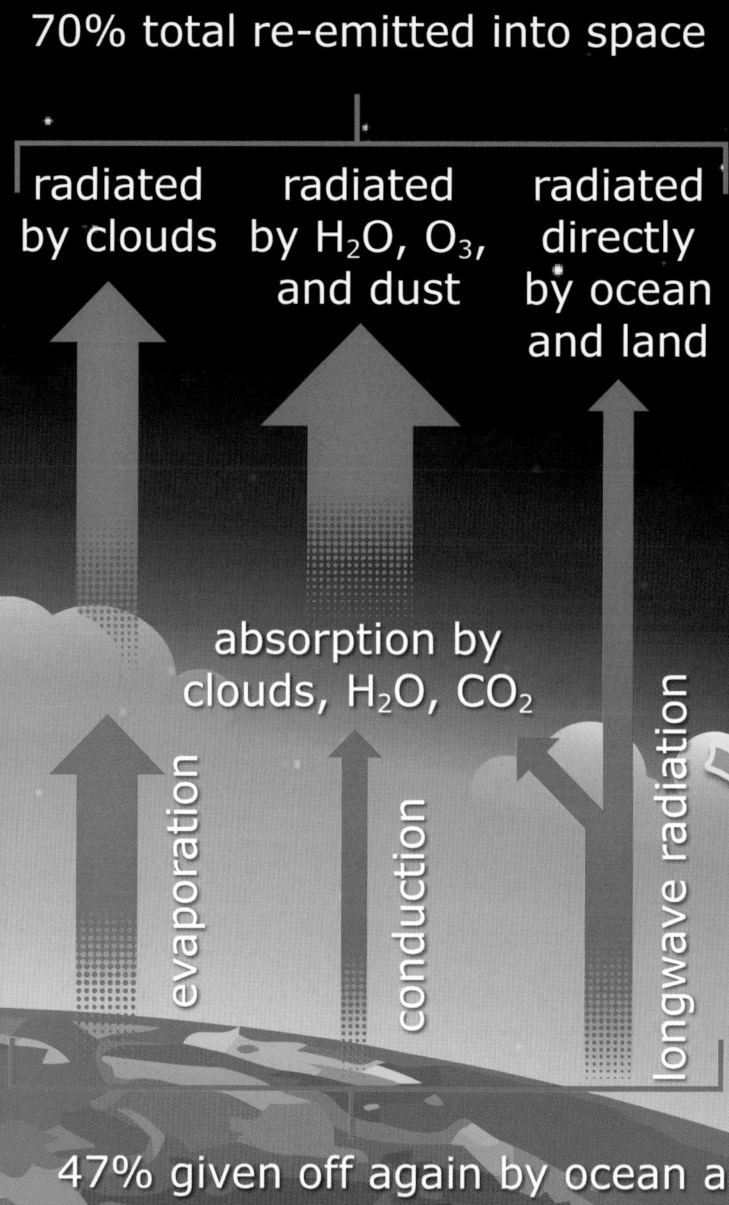

70% total re-emitted into space

radiated by clouds

radiated by H_2O, O_3, and dust

radiated directly by ocean and land

absorption by clouds, H_2O, CO_2

evaporation

conduction

longwave radiation

47% given off again by ocean and land

Heat is radiated directly back into the atmosphere. Land or water can also heat the air above via conduction. And heat is absorbed as water evaporates from Earth's surface and that energy is transferred into the atmosphere as the water vapor rises above Earth's surface.

Earth's Energy Budget

Have you or your family ever been on a budget? The idea of a budget is to plan for both the money that you make (income) and the money you spend (expenses). The Earth system maintains a rough balance between the amount of energy that enters the system from the sun and the amount of energy that leaves the system from Earth. This is called Earth's **energy budget.**

We say that a budget is balanced when you do not spend more money than you make. For Earth's energy budget to be balanced, the amount of solar energy entering Earth's atmosphere should equal the amount released back into space. Look at the diagram and see if the amount of energy entering the Earth system and the amount of energy leaving the system balance out.

If less solar energy leaves the Earth system than enters, Earth's energy budget becomes out of balance and the planet heats up. If more solar energy escapes or is reflected back into space than comes in from the sun, Earth's energy budget becomes out of balance in the other direction. Earth cools down, perhaps becoming too cold for life. At the present time in Earth's history, the energy budget appears to be out of balance. The planet is heating up as more energy is stored near Earth's surface. This is global warming.

Check for Understanding

- Explain the three ways in which heat is transferred.
- What does it mean for Earth's energy budget to be balanced?
- About half of the solar radiation that hits Earth's atmosphere never reaches Earth's surface. What happens to that energy?

The Greenhouse Effect

Earth is habitable because of its atmosphere. Not only does the atmosphere provide air for us to breathe, but it also protects us from the sun's harmful ultraviolet radiation while allowing other wavelengths of the sun's energy to reach Earth's surface. The atmosphere also absorbs and emits enough heat energy from Earth to maintain a temperature where water is usually liquid and life as we know it can function.

When Earth's surface re-radiates and conducts heat back into the atmosphere, not all of it escapes into space. Some of that energy is absorbed by gases in the air, and the air heats up. The energy that might have escaped into space is trapped by the atmosphere. The trapping of heat near the planet's surface by gases in the atmosphere is called the **greenhouse effect**. Water vapor, carbon dioxide, methane, and other gases are all greenhouse gases.

The greenhouse effect is a natural process. Without it, life on Earth would not be possible. A planet the same distance from the sun as Earth, but without an atmosphere like Earth's to act as a natural greenhouse, would be too cold to support life.

So why do we sometimes refer to the greenhouse effect as a problem? Humans are changing the atmosphere, which changes the way Earth's greenhouse effect works. Human activity is releasing large quantities of greenhouse gases — such as carbon dioxide, methane, and nitrous oxides — into the atmosphere. Carbon dioxide occurs naturally, but is also added to the atmosphere as humans burn fossil fuels and manufacture cement. Methane also occurs

naturally, but is emitted in large amounts by industry, livestock, and decaying waste in landfills. The addition of excess greenhouses gases can trap more heat in the atmosphere than is needed. Earth's energy budget becomes unbalanced, and the planet's temperature starts to rise.

Check for Understanding

- In what way is the greenhouse effect essential for life on Earth?

- What change in the atmosphere is making Earth's greenhouse effect into a challenge for humans and life on Earth?

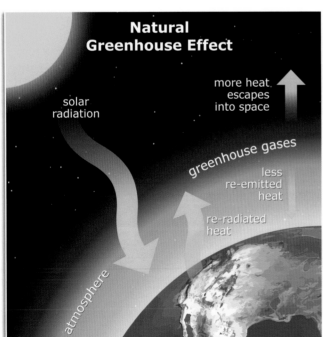

Natural Greenhouse Effect

solar radiation

more heat escapes into space

greenhouse gases

less re-emitted heat

re-radiated heat

atmosphere

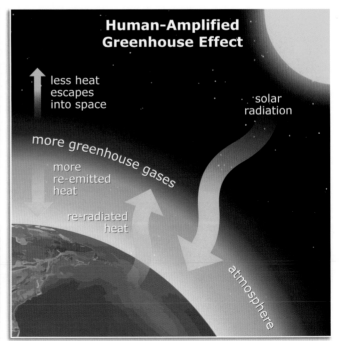

Human-Amplified Greenhouse Effect

less heat escapes into space

solar radiation

more greenhouse gases

more re-emitted heat

re-radiated heat

atmosphere

Heat Transfer and the Greenhouse Effect

Diane Stanitski and other climatologists must fully understand the basics of how heat is transferred so they can explain changes they observe in climate data. In this lab, you will do three demonstrations and explain your observations in terms of conduction, convection, and radiation. You will then apply what you observed to explain the role of the different types of heat transfer in the greenhouse effect.

Materials

- baking dish
- petroleum jelly
- 3 metal brad fasteners
- metal knitting needle, 25 cm (10 in.) long
- ruler
- safety goggles
- tea candle
- pliers
- dishpan filled with water
- towel
- Convection Spiral Sheet
- scissors
- needle
- piece of thread, 20 cm (8 in.) long
- tape
- pencil
- 2 desk lamps with incandescent or halogen bulbs
- small container filled with a layer of coffee grounds 2.5 cm (1 in.) thick

Part 1: Conduction

1. Use a small amount of petroleum jelly to stick the flat head of a metal brad fastener to the knitting needle, at least 5 cm (2 in.) from the pointy end. Stick the remaining two brads to the knitting needle in the same way, lining them up with at least 2 cm (3/4 in.) between each fastener.

2. Place the tea candle on the bottom of the baking dish about 2.5 cm (1 in.) from the edge of one of the short sides of the dish.

3. Based on what you know about conduction, predict what will happen to the brads if you hold the pointy end of the knitting needle in the flame of the candle.

4. Put on your safety goggles.

5. Use the pliers to grasp the knitting needle close to the dull end. Ask your teacher to light the candle for you. Then position the pointy end of the knitting needle just above the flame, making sure you are holding the entire knitting needle over the baking dish. Be sure that the part of the knitting needle where the brads are attached is not over the flame. Hold the knitting needle in place for a few minutes as you record your observations. Remember to always use the pliers to hold the knitting needle; do not touch it with your bare hands at any time.

6. Blow out the candle. Then use the pliers to place the knitting needle into a dishpan of water for at least one minute to cool it down. Use the towel to dry off and clean the knitting needle.

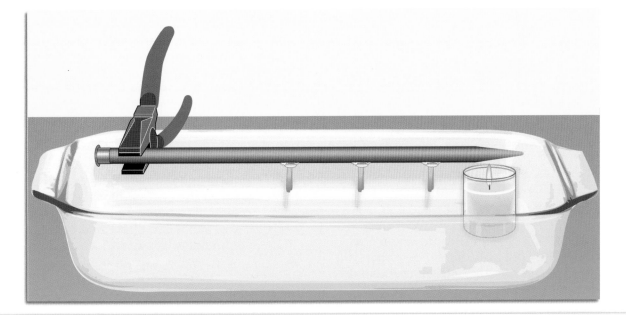

Part 2: Convection

1. Cut out a paper spiral from the Convection Spiral Sheet.

2. Using a needle, insert a piece of thread about 20 cm (8 in.) long through the dot on the center top of the spiral. Tie both ends of the thread to keep the paper from slipping off the thread. Be sure the paper can spin freely around the thread.

3. Tape the top end of the thread to one end of a pencil, so that the spiral hangs off the pencil.

4. Based on your knowledge of convection, predict what will happen if you hold the spiral above a heat source.

5. Point the desk lamp so the light shines straight up. Then turn on the lamp.

6. Hold the pencil so that the spiral hangs above the light, with the bottom of the spiral about 10 cm (4 in.) from the light bulb.

7. Hold the pencil steady, and record your observations.

Part 3: Radiation

1. Place your hand, palm-up, about 10 cm (4 in.) beneath the light bulb of a lamp. Then turn on the lamp and describe what you feel. Be careful not to touch the light bulb!

2. Remove your hand, and place a small container filled with a layer of coffee grounds 2.5 cm (1 in.) thick under the lamp. The light bulb should be about 10 cm (4 in.) above the coffee grounds and should point directly onto the grounds.

3. Based on what you know about radiation, predict what will happen to the coffee grounds if you leave them under the lamp for a few minutes.

4. After 5 minutes, move the container of coffee grounds out from under the light. Place your hand about 2 cm (3/4 in.) above the coffee grounds. Record your observations.

Reflect and Apply

1. Use what you know about conduction to explain what you observed in Part 1.

2. Use what you know about convection to explain what you observed in Part 2.

3. Use what you know about radiation to explain what you observed in Part 3.

4. Based on your observations of the types of heat transfer and your knowledge of the greenhouse effect, explain the role of heat transfer in creating the greenhouse effect on Earth.

Extension

Materials absorb and re-radiate heat differently. Gather a variety of materials and predict which will absorb and re-radiate more heat. Be sure to explain your rationale. Then design a way to test how well the materials absorb and re-radiate heat. Conduct the test and compare the results with your prediction.

Journal Question

How is understanding basic processes such as conduction, convection, and radiation important for understanding the greenhouse effect and other more complex Earth system processes?

Your expedition goal is accomplished when you: Know and can describe the causes and patterns of Earth's global winds.

Can explain how ocean surface currents form and where major gyres are located.

Why this is important: Understanding surface currents and the global winds that create them allows us to better understand the factors affecting Earth's climates.

Words to identify: air pressure, wind, trade winds, doldrums, prevailing westerlies, polar easterlies, Coriolis effect, surface current, gyre, Gulf Stream, eddies, upwelling

Stage 2: Wind Blows, Water Flows

So much of what interests Diane Stanitski about climate happens at the boundary between Earth's atmosphere and ocean. This is where energy is exchanged. This is where great quantities of water evaporate into the air or fall back as rain. This is where oxygen can make its way into the air and carbon dioxide can dissolve into the sea. And this is where great winds blow across the water, creating the surface currents on which Stanitski's drifting buoys travel, transmitting back data.

Air Pressure and Local Winds

Although you cannot see it, you live at the bottom of an "ocean" of air. Air is far from nothing. Air is composed of nitrogen, oxygen, carbon dioxide, water vapor, and many other different molecules and atoms, all in a gaseous state. Each of those atoms and molecules has mass and is pulled toward Earth's center by gravity. **Air pressure** is the force per unit area exerted on a surface by the weight of the air above that surface. Altitude affects air pressure. The higher up you go, the fewer air molecules are above you, and therefore air pressure is lower.

Air pressure is lower at a higher altitude because a shorter column of air pushes down.

Fast Fact

Mountain climbing is difficult under the best of circumstances. But when it comes to climbing one of Earth's highest mountains, such as Mount Everest, the challenges become outright dangerous. Avalanches and temperatures well below freezing make the climb treacherous. Now imagine making that climb with little oxygen to inhale. You can become exhausted just from trying to breathe. Climbers refer to elevations above 8,000 m (26,000 ft) as "the death zone." Oxygen levels in the thin air are only one-third what they are at sea level. While some hardcore climbers have successfully climbed Everest without oxygen tanks, most climbers need oxygen masks and tanks above 8,000 m.

Air pressure is higher at a lower altitude because a taller column of air pushes down.

▶ An imaginary column of air extends above Earth's surface. Within that column, there are fewer and fewer molecules of atmospheric gases per volume of air the higher you go. That is why air pressure decreases with altitude.

The sun heats the land, which heats the air above. The warm air rises, creating an area of low air pressure.

The sun also heats the ocean water, but the ocean remains cooler than the land during the day because of water's high heat capacity. Air sinks over the ocean, creating an area of high air pressure.

L

H

A local wind, called a sea breeze, is created by air moving from the high-pressure area located over the ocean, toward the low-pressure area over the land.

Air pressure also changes when the air itself is heated or cooled, as this causes the air to expand or contract, changing its density. For example, air pressure differences can result from the uneven heating of Earth's surface and the air just above. Let's say an area of land — a beach, for example — is warmed by the sun's energy. Much of the energy from the sun is absorbed by the sand and then re-emitted, heating the air above. As the air gets hotter, the molecules in the air move faster and spread out, making the air less dense. Because warm air is less dense than the surrounding air, the warm air rises, moving away from Earth's surface. This produces a local area of low pressure. If an air mass cools, the molecules in the air slow down and pack more closely together, making the air denser. Cold air sinks, producing a local area of high pressure.

Wind is the horizontal movement of air from a high-pressure area to a low-pressure area. The pressure difference between two air masses is what causes wind to blow. You can think of it as air moving from a place that has too much air to a place that has too little air. Wind is what you feel when the air rushes by you, moving between the two places. Wind speed depends on how large the pressure difference is between the two areas. The greater the pressure difference between the two locations, the faster the wind blows. Winds are always named for the direction from which they blow. A north wind — or northerly — blows from the north toward the south.

Global Winds

Look back at the diagram of Earth's energy budget. The diagram shows a lot, but simplifies a few things. For example, it shows the sun's rays coming in and striking one part of Earth's surface at an angle. How is the real Earth different from that model?

Earth is basically a sphere. When the sun is at its zenith — that is, directly overhead — the sun's energy is striking Earth's surface most directly. The rays are perpendicular to Earth's surface. As you move away from perpendicular, solar energy strikes Earth's surface in a less direct way. At lower angles, the same amount of energy is being spread out over a greater

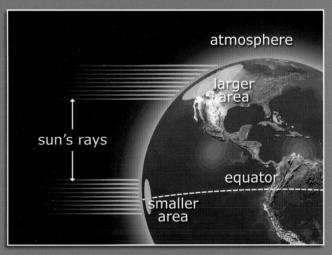

As latitude increases, heating from the sun decreases as the same amount of solar energy is spread out over greater areas.

surface area, reducing the intensity at any one point. Earth's surface heats less when there is less solar energy striking the same size area. At low latitudes near the equator, more solar energy is available to be absorbed than at higher latitudes, such as the North and South Poles. Therefore, more heating occurs at low latitudes near the equator.

Understanding global winds is complex, but we can begin by imagining Earth as a small, smooth sphere that is not rotating. With sunlight hitting the equator of this sphere at a 90° angle, the greatest heating of the sphere's surface — and of the air above — would occur near the equator. Warm air over the equator would rise, resulting in low air pressure. Air pressure would be high at the poles where cold air would sink. The difference in air pressure would cause winds at the sphere's surface to blow from the poles toward the equator. Higher up in the atmosphere, air would flow back from the equator toward the poles, completing a large loop.

Global Wind Circulation

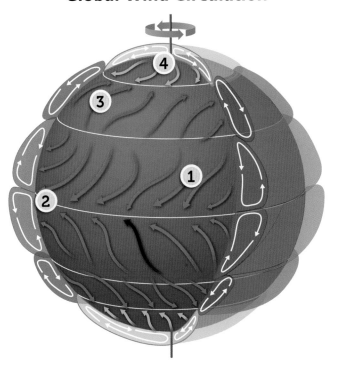

1. The **trade winds** are found between the equator and approximately 30° latitude in both hemispheres. These steady, consistent winds are easterlies, which means they blow from east to west.

2. The **doldrums** are areas of little or no wind at the equator. Air is rising here, so there is little horizontal air movement (wind). There are also zones of little wind at approximately 30° latitude in both hemispheres where air is sinking. These are called the horse latitudes.

3. Westerlies blow from west to east in the mid-latitudes. The **prevailing westerlies** are found between approximately 30° and 60° latitude in both hemispheres.

4. The **polar easterlies** are cold, dry winds that move around the polar regions. They blow from east to west between approximately 60° and 90° latitude in both hemispheres.

Global Winds

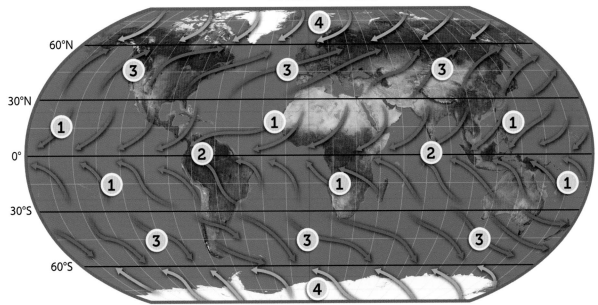

Of course, this model is too simple. Global winds would flow directly from the poles to the equator only if Earth did not spin on its axis. The motion of Earth spinning on its axis causes winds to follow a curved path. Earth rotates from west to east. The paths of the global winds appear to bend or deflect to the right in the Northern Hemisphere and to the left in the Southern Hemisphere. This apparent deflection of movement from an expected straight path due to Earth's rotation is called the **Coriolis effect**. The Coriolis effect and pressure differences in Earth's atmosphere create Earth's global winds.

Try This!

Find a partner for this activity. Blow up and knot a round balloon. This is your model Earth. Use a marker to draw an equator line around the balloon's middle. Mark the top of the balloon with an "N" to make the North Pole and the bottom of the balloon with an "S" to make the South Pole. On the top of the balloon, draw a small arrow pointing from west to east (counter-clockwise when viewed from above). Now try to draw a line from the North Pole straight down to the equator. As you begin to draw, have your partner slowly turn the balloon in the direction of the arrow. Keep trying to draw your line south to the equator, but do not lift the marker or resist the motion of the balloon. Stop drawing at the equator. Trade jobs with your partner. Turn the balloon in the direction of the arrow as your partner tries to draw a line from the South Pole straight up to the equator. What happened as you and your partner tried to draw straight lines? Why?

Check for Understanding

- What causes wind?
- Explain how winds are deflected due to Earth's rotation.

Ocean Surface Currents

Have you ever been to a lake on a calm, windless day? If so, you might have observed that the water looked as smooth as glass. Later, if a wind started blowing across the lake, you might have noticed ripples on the water's surface. The stronger the wind and the larger the lake, the larger the ripples would have been. The friction of air moving across the water's surface causes water to move.

On a larger scale, the strong global winds that blow across Earth's oceans create large surface currents in the water. A **surface current** is a large stream of water moving along at the ocean's surface. The winds start to move the water where the air moves across the water's surface, but surface currents can extend down several hundred meters deep. About 10% of the ocean's water is being moved in surface currents at any one time.

▼ Earth's surface currents form large, oval-shaped loops called gyres. Do you see the similarity between surface current movements and the movements of Earth's global winds?

Global Surface Currents

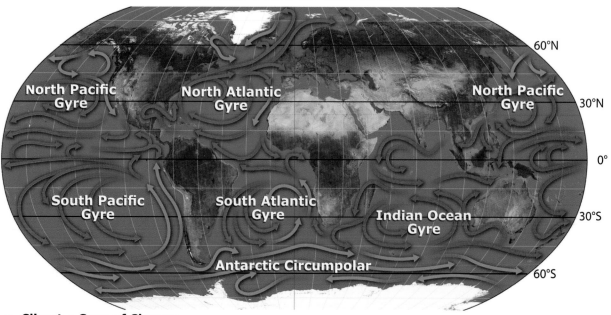

If surface currents are caused by the global winds, you might expect the surface current paths to resemble the global wind paths. And they do, with some modifications. The Coriolis effect causes surface currents in the Northern Hemisphere to be deflected to the right and currents in the Southern Hemisphere to be deflected to the left. In addition, surface currents cannot flow through land. Instead, ocean surface currents are blocked and deflected by Earth's continents.

Gyres

The most obvious pattern to Earth's surface currents is that of large loops. The large, oval-shaped surface current loops are called **gyres**. There are two gyres in the Pacific Ocean — one each in the northern and southern Pacific. Likewise, there are two gyres in the Atlantic Ocean, one each on either side of the equator. A fifth gyre is located in the Indian Ocean.

Each gyre is made up of a series of currents that flow into each other:

1. Closest to the equator are the equatorial currents. The equatorial currents are created by the trade winds and move from east to west, north and south of the equator.

2. On the west side of each ocean basin, the gyre encounters land, splits, and turns away from the equator, along the continent's eastern edge. This is where you find the western boundary currents.

3. The western boundary currents continue moving away from the equator and toward higher latitudes until they reach the latitudes of the prevailing westerlies. These currents move water from west to east across the ocean basin.

4. Finally, on the eastern side of the ocean basin, the currents again reach a continent and move back toward the equator, forming the eastern boundary currents.

Surface Current Temperatures

One of the data instruments on the drifting buoys that Diane Stanitski uses is a thermistor — a type of temperature sensor. Located in the bottom of the drifter, the thermistor measures ocean surface-water temperature. Measuring sea surface temperature is important in predicting climate patterns and changes because the ocean's currents transfer so much energy.

Fast Fact

"Follow that duckie!" It may be hard to believe, but bath toys helped scientists figure out something about surface currents they had not known before. In 1992, a cargo ship on its way from Hong Kong to the United States lost a container of plastic bath toys in the middle of the northern Pacific Ocean. Ten months later, plastic ducks and frogs began to wash up on the shores of Alaska. The hunt was on to find more bath toys hitting the shores elsewhere. More than half the toys took currents south and traveled back across the Pacific on the equatorial current or worked their way down the coast of South America. Scientists were able to follow the progress of the toys in the northern route and, using this low-tech approach, figured out for the first time that the water in the North Pacific Gyre takes three years to make a complete loop.

Surface currents are said to be warm currents or cold currents based on the temperature of the water moving in them. Equatorial currents form nearest the equator where solar heating is the greatest, so those are warm currents. The western boundary currents, such as the Gulf Stream in the North Atlantic Gyre, start near the equator, so they are also warm water currents. The **Gulf Stream** runs along the east coast of North America and is an extremely warm current.

Due to unequal heating in the Northern and Southern Hemispheres, the currents moving toward the equator are cold currents while the currents moving toward the poles are warm currents.

▲ In this image generated by a state-of-the-art computer climate model, warmer water is red and cooler water is blue. You can see the warm Gulf Stream moving north along the eastern coast of the United States before moving off into the Atlantic Ocean toward western Europe.

Global Drifter Program Drifting Buoy

tether

1 meter

The NOAA Adopt a Drifter Program, coordinated by Diane Stanitski, enables schools to adopt buoys that are part of a larger, global, ocean observing system supported by the United States and many international partners. Schools have been adopting drifters since December 2004. The countries in the Data Buoy Co-operation Panel sustain approximately 1,000 drifters in the ocean. Data from all the buoys are gathered, shared, and made available for real-time analysis. According to Stanitski, "Our mission is to make observations, collect data, analyze the data, and apply what we learn so we can discover more about our climate, how it changes, and how it impacts our global communities."

The Global Drifter Program (GDP) supports drifting buoys that are designed to float and move with the ocean's currents. Other buoys in the global system are moored in place and anchored to the bottom of the ocean.

Size:

The drifting buoy's spherical surface float is about 40 cm (16 in.) in diameter. The drogue, or sea anchor, is suspended some 15 m (49 ft) below the float to keep the drifter moving in the ocean currents and not pushed along by the wind. The drogue is made of nylon cloth with sections totaling about 6.5 m (21 ft).

Toolkit:

Data Sensors – All drifters measure sea surface temperature, and some measure air pressure, wind speed and direction, salinity, and ocean color.

Drifter Location – The position of a drifter is not usually given by the familiar Global Positioning System (GPS). Instead, it is inferred from the Doppler shift of its transmission as seen by a satellite above.

Data Transmitter – Each drifter sends sensor data to a satellite before the data eventually make it to the Drifter Data Assembly Center (DAC) in Miami, Florida, to be prepared for use by researchers.

Drogue – Creates drag underwater and causes the buoy to be pulled along by ocean currents instead of wind and waves

Battery Pack – Powers the drifter for about 400 days

drogue

Eddies

Take a closer look at the image of the Gulf Stream generated by a computer climate model. Does the Gulf Stream look like a river to you? Rivers have features called meanders and so does the Gulf Stream. Meanders are snake-like bends in a river. In rivers, erosion and deposition can enlarge and eventually cut meanders off from the main river channel, forming ox-bow lakes.

Meanders in large surface currents sometimes wrap around so much that they close over on themselves, forming a ring-shaped current that gets cut off from the main current. These smaller currents are called **eddies** or rings. Depending on which side of the main current the rings form, they can have either a cold-water core surrounded by warm water or a warm-water core surrounded by cold water.

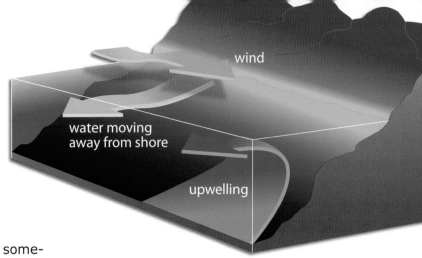

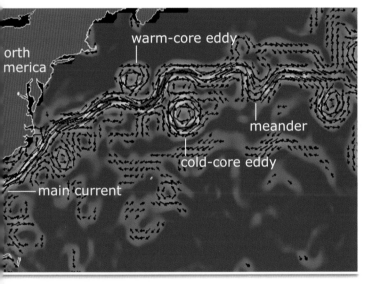

▲ This map of Gulf Stream surface current velocities is based on satellite data. Red and yellow indicate the fastest moving water.

Upwelling

Upwelling is the vertical movement of cold, nutrient-rich water from the deep ocean to the ocean's surface. Upwelling is very important, as the nutrients brought up with the cold water support the growth of phytoplankton, which are the base of the marine food web. For instance, krill eat the plankton. Whales, fish, and squid eat the krill. And dolphins and seabirds feed on the fish and squid. Upwelling supports a rich abundance of marine organisms.

Some upwelling occurs at Earth's equator where winds cause the surface waters to move apart, creating a gap that allows cold, deep water to rise to the surface. This equatorial upwelling creates some of the best fishing grounds in the world.

Upwelling also occurs along coasts where coastal winds run parallel to the shoreline. The effect of Earth's rotation on the wind moving along the shoreline is to move water near the ocean's surface away from the shore. This allows cold, deep water to rise up from below to replace the surface water. This type of upwelling occurs off the west coasts of both North America and South America. In San Francisco, the upwelling brings in the cold water that results in plentiful fog and lower ocean temperatures. Off the coasts of California and Oregon, upwelling is seasonal, typically lasting from spring until the end of summer each year.

Fast Fact

The Northern Hemisphere is warmer than the Southern Hemisphere. Why? First, Antarctica is very big and reflects a lot more of the sun's energy back into space than the less icy Arctic Ocean. The Northern Hemisphere also has more land in the tropical latitudes. Land absorbs and re-radiates more of the sun's energy into the atmosphere than water. Finally, in the Atlantic Ocean, some warm water from the Southern Hemisphere moves across the equator into the Northern Hemisphere. The net effect is that the Northern Hemisphere is warmer.

Check for Understanding

- Which surface currents are formed by the trade winds?

- How is the pattern of ocean surface currents different from the pattern of Earth's global winds?

- Why would some of the best whale watching along the central California coast happen in the summer?

Ocean Surface Currents

When Diane Stanitski and John Adler helped the JASON Argonauts launch two drifting buoys off the coast of California, they relied on their knowledge of ocean surface currents to identify good places to launch the buoys and to predict where the buoys would go. However, as the Argonauts discovered, many factors can affect currents at specific points in time, and predicting the path of a buoy is not always easy. In this lab, you will simulate ocean surface currents and observe the effects of wind and land masses on those currents. Then you will create your own new world and map its wind patterns and surface currents. You will select a launching point for a drifting buoy and predict and observe its movements.

Materials
- **Global Surface Currents map (p. 56)**
- **Global Winds map (p. 55)**
- **baking dish, 23 x 33 cm (9 x 13 in.)**
- **water**
- **pepper**
- **2 bendable straws**
- **colored pencils (red, blue, green, orange, and black)**
- **rocks of assorted sizes**
- **scissors**
- **safety goggles**

Part 1: Practice Creating Surface Currents

1. Study the Global Surface Currents map. What patterns do you notice?

2. Compare the Global Surface Currents map to the Global Winds map. What relationships do you observe between the wind patterns and the surface currents?

3. Fill a baking dish half way with water. Put on your safety goggles. Then lightly sprinkle pepper on top of the water.

4. Bend a straw, and hold the short, bent end just above the surface of the water, with the long end sticking up. Practice blowing gently through the straw across the surface of the water to simulate wind moving across ocean water. Place the straw as close to the water as possible, and adjust the angle of the straw so the air moves across the water rather than into it. When done correctly, you should see the pepper moving on the surface of the water.

Part 2: Predict and Observe Surface Currents

1. Predict how the water will move if you and a partner blow gently through two straws across the surface of the water from opposite corners of the baking dish. Draw your prediction, using blue arrows to show the direction of the wind and red arrows to show the movement of the water. Label the drawing "Corner Currents Prediction."

2. Work with a partner to blow gently across the water's surface from opposite corners of the baking dish. Try to blow with the same force as your partner. Have a third group member closely observe the movement of the water. (The pepper will make this easier to see.) Draw the movement of the water, using the same color scheme as in the previous step. Label the drawing "Corner Currents Results."

3. Place a rock in the center of the baking dish to represent a land mass. The rock should be large enough to stick up above the surface of the water. Predict how the water will move if you blow gently across the surface of the water, as in the previous step. Draw your prediction, using the color scheme from the previous steps and black to draw the rock. Label your drawing "Corner Currents with Land Mass Prediction."

④ Again blow across the surface of the water as you did in step 2. Observe the movement of the water. Draw the movement of the water, and label the drawing "Corner Currents with Land Mass Results."

⑤ Compare your predictions and results. Was the water movement different from what you expected? Do you see any patterns in your results?

Part 3: Map Surface Currents

① Using rocks to simulate land masses, create a new world in the baking dish. Draw a map of your world, using black for the land masses. Label your map with the name of your world and the names of the land masses. Label north on your map.

② Choose two locations, on opposite sides of the baking dish, from which the wind will blow in your new world. Show the direction of the wind on your map using blue arrows.

③ Predict the movement of the water as the "wind" blows in the directions shown on your map. Draw your prediction on your map, using red arrows to show the movement of the water. Label your map with the name of your world and the words "Surface Currents Prediction."

④ Draw a second copy of your map showing the land masses and wind directions. Gently blow across the surface of the water from the two directions shown on your map. Observe the movement of the water. Draw the movement of the water on your map, using red arrows. You may need to do this several times to correctly trace the movement of the water. Label your map with the name of your world and the words "Surface Currents Results."

Part 4: Launch a Drifting Buoy

① Cut a 2-cm (3/4-in.) piece from the end of one of the straws. This will be your drifting buoy. Carefully study the surface currents shown on your Surface Currents Results map. Select a location from which to launch your drifting buoy so that your buoy will stay afloat gathering data as long as possible without hitting a land mass. Using the green colored pencil, draw the path you predict your buoy will take on your Surface Currents Results map.

② Use the straws to gently blow across the surface of the water exactly as you did in Part 3, step 4. Be sure to keep the wind steady; do not change the angle or speed of the wind. Launch your buoy and observe its movements. Using the orange colored pencil, draw the movement of the buoy on your Surface Currents Results map.

Reflect and Apply

① Did your buoy move as you expected? Why or why not?

② How closely did the buoy follow the movement of the surface currents in your world?

③ What patterns do you observe in the surface currents on your Surface Currents Results map?

④ How are the surface current patterns on your two Results drawings from Part 2 and your Surface Currents Results map from Part 3 similar to the surface current patterns on Earth? How are they different? How can you explain these similarities and differences?

⑤ How is the world you created in the simulation different from Earth? Which is more complex? Explain.

Extension

Attempt to improve the performance of your buoy by selecting a new launching point. Predict and test the movement of your buoy from that new point. Consider other factors that could affect the surface currents in the world you created. Design and conduct a test to see how changing one of these factors would affect the surface currents. Be sure to draw your predictions and results.

Journal Question
Explain the relationship between global wind patterns and ocean surface currents on Earth.

In This Stage:

Your expedition goal is accomplished when you:

Know the difference between weather and climate.

Can name and describe the six major climate zones.

Why this is important:

Understanding "normal" climate and climate variability is critical to being able to recognize climate change as it occurs.

Words to identify:

weather, climate, tropical climate, savanna, dry climate, desert, steppe, temperate marine climate, temperate continental climate, permafrost, polar climate, tundra, highlands climate

Stage 3: Temperate to Tundra

The American writer Mark Twain once said, "Climate is what we expect, weather is what we get." Climate is not the same thing as weather. **Weather** describes conditions, such as temperature and wind, at a specific place at a moment in time. Weather describes what is happening outside your window right now. **Climate** refers to the average weather conditions for a location over a long period of time.

Climate is what you might *expect* to be happening outside your window this time of year. For example, if you live in New Jersey, you may not know what the weather is like today in Tampa, Florida. You could call friends or family who live in Tampa and ask them to look outside. Or you could get online and look up current weather conditions for Tampa. However, what you probably do know is that it is probably warmer in Tampa at any given time than it is in New Jersey. Tampa simply has a different climate. You probably also know that Phoenix, Arizona, is hot and dry. Its climate — which is different from the climates in New Jersey and Tampa — has been fairly stable year after year.

What is considered a long enough period of time for weather conditions to be called climate? Climatologists, such as Diane Stanitski, often use climate "normals" when referring to current climate conditions. The most general definition of a climate "normal" is the average of climate measurements, such as temperature or precipitation, taken at a location over a 30-year period. Generally, this includes the last three consecutive decades.

Climate Types

Earth has different climates because its surface is heated unequally by the sun. More solar energy is available to be absorbed at low latitudes near the equator, so more heating occurs at those latitudes. Less heating occurs at high latitudes near the poles. Therefore, hotter climates are found near the equator and colder climates are found near the poles.

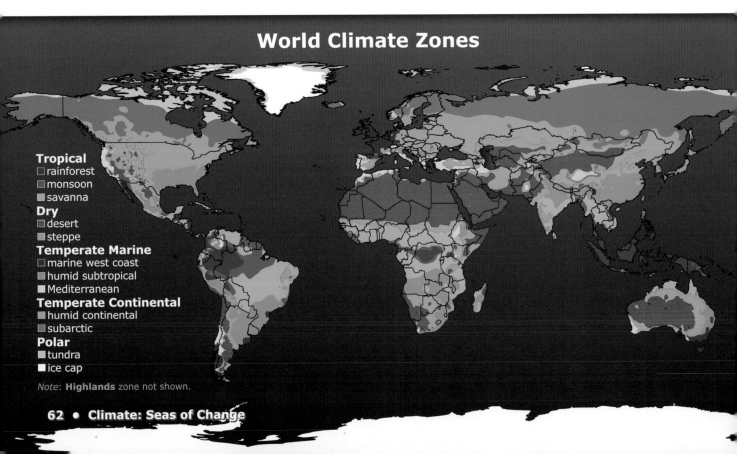

World Climate Zones

Tropical
☐ rainforest
☐ monsoon
■ savanna
Dry
☐ desert
■ steppe
Temperate Marine
☐ marine west coast
■ humid subtropical
■ Mediterranean
Temperate Continental
■ humid continental
☐ subarctic
Polar
■ tundra
■ ice cap

Note: **Highlands** zone not shown.

Although there are several systems for classifying specific climate types, or zones, the most widely used system is the Köppen system, which uses average monthly temperature and precipitation. The Köppen system has been modified over time to create slightly different climate systems. One such modified system divides Earth's land masses into six main climate zones: tropical, dry, temperate marine, temperate continental, polar, and highlands. These six climate zones are then sub-divided into smaller sub-zones. The Köppen system is still popular more than 125 years after it was first published because the zones and sub-zones correspond to observable differences in soil types and communities of plants and animals.

Tropical

What do you think of when you hear the word "tropical"? Palm trees? White sandy beaches? What then do you think makes a climate tropical? If you look at the climate zone map, you will notice that the tropical climate sub-zones are all located at low latitudes — that is, near the equator where Earth is warmest. Tropical typically means hot and humid. In **tropical climates**, the average temperature in the coolest month of the year does not get below 18°C (64°F).

The tropical climate zone is divided into three sub-zones based on differences in precipitation. The tropical rainforest climate is the wettest of the tropical climates. Here it rains almost every day, often with heavy afternoon thunderstorms. As the name implies, this is the climate where you would expect to find tropical rainforests. The next tropical climate is known for tropical grasslands called **savannas**. The tropical savanna climate gets less rain than the rainforest sub-zone, but experiences wet and dry seasons. Tropical savannas are found in Africa, South America, India, and Southeast Asia. Tropical savanna covers parts of northern Australia as well. Finally, there is the tropical monsoon climate where it is warm all year long, but the heavy monsoon rains come only during the summer when the land heats up and the strong monsoon winds pull in moisture and precipitation from the nearby ocean. This climate is common in Southeast Asia, but is also found in parts of Mexico, South America, and Africa.

Dry

Dry climates are a bit more complicated. Temperature is not the primary determining condition for dry climates. You can find dry climates in both warm and cold parts of the world. A **dry climate** is one where the precipitation that falls to Earth from clouds has a good chance of being completely taken back up into the air again by evaporation and transpiration.

The most obvious of the dry climates is the **desert**. Again, remember that temperature is not the determining factor. You can have a cold, rocky desert just as easily as a hot, sandy desert. On average, a desert climate receives less than 25 cm (10 in.) of rain each year. There is variability within that. Some years, there might be no precipitation at all. Examples of hot deserts are the Sahara in Africa and the Mojave Desert in southeastern California. A large region of Australia is covered by hot desert as well. The Gobi Desert in China and the Great Basin Desert in the western United States are examples of cold deserts. Most deserts are found at about 30° to 35° North and South latitudes — the horse latitudes — where global wind cells meet and dry air descends.

A slightly less dry climate is the **steppe**. The steppe climate is usually found near or bordering the desert climates. Steppes are often dry, flat areas covered with grasses and short bushes. In the United States, the prairies of the Great Plains are located in a dry steppe climate. The Pampas of southeastern South America are found in a slightly warmer steppe climate.

Temperate Marine

People who are "temperate" do not display extreme behaviors. They are calm and even-keeled. Similarly, a temperate climate is one that is calmer than it is extreme. Temperate climates are found in Earth's temperate zones — the geographical areas between the tropics and the polar regions. Because of their latitude, temperate zones have clearly defined seasons. Temperate climates can either be affected by the nearby ocean — the temperate marine climates — or affected less by the ocean — the temperate continental climates.

In the case of **temperate marine climates**, the nearby presence of the ocean moderates the temperatures and precipitation during the year. Winters are mild and there is enough water in the air to produce precipitation — in the form of rain or snow — throughout the year. The three temperate marine climate sub-zones are marine west coast, humid subtropical, and Mediterranean.

The west coast of Canada, most of western Europe, and the west coast of Chile in southern South America are all part of the marine west coast climate. This climate is affected by cold surface currents that move along the western continental coasts. In the marine west coast climate, summers are milder than you might expect for the latitude.

The humid subtropical climates are warm and found next to the true tropical climates. These are the warmest of the temperate climates. Summers here are hot and humid. Winters are cool to mild. The southeastern United States is part of this climate zone as are much of southeastern China and southeastern South America.

Parts of Europe and northern Africa bordering the Mediterranean Sea have a Mediterranean climate. There are cool, rainy winters and warm, dry summers. The coast of California also has a Mediterranean climate.

Temperate Continental

Temperate continental climates occur within large continents, away from the immediate effects of the ocean and ocean currents. These climates occur only in the temperate zones of the Northern Hemisphere. There are not any temperate continental climates found in the Southern Hemisphere because the two large, southern continents, South America and Africa, taper toward the South Pole. The continents are so narrow west-to-east in the temperate zone latitudes that there is no land unaffected by the nearby ocean and ocean currents.

The temperate continental climate is divided into the humid continental and subarctic climates and is found only in the Northern Hemisphere. The humid continental climate zone has well-defined seasons, with weather influenced by air masses that move in from the poles or the tropics. Winters are cold or even severely cold due to polar air masses sliding in from the north. In the summer, tropical air masses from the south bring heat and high humidity. In the United States, this climate stretches from the Midwest all the way to New England. It is also found stretching east from central Europe into central Asia.

North of the humid continental climates are the subarctic climates of Alaska, Canada, Scandinavia, and northern Russia. Summers here are short and cool. Winters are long and very cold. For more than half the year, average daily temperatures are below freezing. The soil freezes, and only the upper part thaws in the warmer months. The permanently frozen soil is called **permafrost**. There is not much precipitation in the subarctic. The dominant pine trees do not release as much water as deciduous trees and are able to hold on to the water they have.

Polar

Naturally, the coldest climates occur at or near Earth's poles. The **polar climate** is divided into tundra and ice cap climates.

Like the temperate continental climates, the **tundra** climate occurs only in the Northern Hemisphere. It is found north of the subarctic climate in Alaska, Canada, and northern Russia. In the tundra, summers are short and cool. Winters are long and extremely cold. The tundra soil is permafrost. Vegetation is limited to grasses, moss, and small shrubs.

The most extreme climate on Earth is the ice cap. In the Northern Hemisphere, there is an ice cap climate on Greenland. Antarctica is entirely an ice cap. The temperatures in the ice cap climate are almost always below freezing, and there are large sheets of ice which can be covered with thick accumulations of snow.

Highlands

The **highlands climate** is not determined by latitude or distance from the ocean, but rather is defined by elevation. Tall mountains and mountain ranges have their own climate or range of climates. This is because as elevation increases, air pressure decreases and temperatures drop. Near a mountain's base, the climate is the same as the climate zone nearby. But the temperature and humidity decrease as you go higher up the mountain. On the top of a tall mountain, any snow that falls may never melt. The steep slopes on mountains also affect temperature. Incoming sunlight is usually spread out over large areas where mountains have steep slopes. Other parts of the mountain might be in constant shadow, never getting any direct sunlight.

Climate Variability

Climate zones can vary in size. A desert can cover much of a continent, such as in Australia. But a climate can also cover an area as small as a garden or a city park. A microclimate is a local area where the climate differs from the surrounding climate. The city of San Francisco is known for its microclimates. Because of the many hills that cut off one area of the city from another, temperatures at the same time of day can vary by as much as 5°C (9°F) from one side of a hill to the other.

If you live near what looks like a boundary between climates on a climate zone map, you may experience aspects of more than one climate. That is because there are no hard boundaries between climates. The climates blend into one another. This year, your local climate might seem more tropical than temperate. Last year, perhaps it was just the opposite.

Normally, you should think of climate as long term. Think of Buffalo, New York, and remember Mark Twain. In any given January, you would be right to expect Buffalo to be cold and have plenty of snow. Finding one January out of a dozen when Buffalo did not get significant snow would be unusual, but it would not change your well-informed idea that Buffalo has snowy Januarys. Actual average temperatures and precipitation amounts in an area vary from year to year, and are sometimes lower and sometimes higher than the long-term averages. Boston can have a warm January day, and Orlando can have an ice storm. That is not climate change.

Climate change is when the same type of change keeps happening, resulting in an increasing or decreasing trend over time. The warmer January last year is followed by an even warmer January this year. Eventually, when you do the averaging of the data from the last three decades, the new climate normal is different from the old climate normal. On a large scale, climate variability is based on changes in our global patterns of air movement and ocean circulation.

Check for Understanding

- Describe how Earth is divided into climate zones.
- Why are temperate continental climates found only in the Northern Hemisphere?

STEM Spotlight

John Adler

Career: Systems Engineer and Aircraft Navigator
Born: Louisiana
Education: B.A., B.S., University of California, Santa Barbara
Ph.D., University of Colorado, Boulder

A former Navy aerial navigator, John Adler has been on many scientific expeditions, flying crews of scientists throughout the Antarctic and the Arctic. It was often challenging work just finding a safe place to land the plane on the ice sheet! Scientists would brave the harsh, polar temperatures to quickly set up makeshift field laboratories and core into the glacial ice. After joining NOAA, Adler would fly the "Hurricane Hunter" planes in and out of fierce hurricanes along the eastern and Gulf coasts of North America.

Today, Adler is programming and flying remote-controlled Unmanned Aircraft Systems (UAS) in extreme locations, such as Greenland and the Arctic. "The biggest challenge is ensuring that all the sensors and systems will operate without failing. Once the UAS plane is launched, there isn't anyone on board to make changes." Adler knows that using autonomous data collection devices often allows for data collection in harsh conditions. Finding new ways of using advanced technology to solve a problem is one of the most rewarding parts of his job.

Adler intends to fly UAS planes over the Arctic Ocean sea ice to explore the extent of melting related to climate change. "Knowing how the sea ice is changing helps everyone — scientists and citizens — better understand the future of the Arctic and how changes there might affect their own parts of the world."

Adler with the Silver Fox UAS at the end of a photo mission over Greenland's Jakobshavn Glacier

Q & A

What were you like as a kid?
I was always taking electronic and mechanical devices apart. It would drive my mom crazy. However, she did like that I could fix just about anything!

Describe a typical day for you when you are out in the field.
I get up early to launch the unmanned aircraft or to fly in a plane. After the flights, we spend time downloading data into our computers and reviewing the results.

Then what is a not-so-typical day like?
Trying to land on a remote part of the Antarctic ice sheet and finding out you can't take off! After about 17 attempts, we finally got in the air, but we had to offload the scientific gear.

So you get to go to some interesting places in your job?
Definitely! I have been to the South Pole and I have flown over the sea ice at the North Pole. And on the warmer side, I have flown through the eyes of hurricanes 85 times. The variety of places a researcher can go is pretty amazing.

What advice would you give a student interested in pursuing a career in engineering and remote sensing?
Classes are important, but you should also get out and get involved with extracurricular organizations such as the *FIRST* robotics competitions or local "maker" groups. Ask questions about things you don't understand and be willing to get help from others. I wouldn't have made it without the help of fellow students and industry professionals.

Lab 2.3

Comparing Climates

The data that Diane Stanitski and other scientists gather from various ocean buoys help us to better understand the role of the ocean in Earth's climate. In this lab, you will compare the climates of cities at similar latitudes and look for patterns that show how nearness to the ocean affects climate.

Materials
- **Blank World Map**
- **World Climate Zones map (p. 62)**
- **Global Surface Currents map (p. 56)**
- **Climate Data Fact Sheet**
- **2 copies of Climograph Template**

Part 1: Predicting Climate

1. Use a world map to locate the following cities: Tokyo, Japan; Xian, China; Arica, Chile; Santa Cruz de la Sierra, Bolivia; Trondheim, Norway; and Yakutsk, Russia. Mark the location and name of these cities on the Blank World Map.

2. Compare the location of these cities to the World Climate Zones map. Record the name of the climate zone where each city is located on the Blank World Map.

3. Find the location of the three coastal cities on the Global Surface Currents map. Record the kinds of currents nearest each city on the Blank World Map.

4. Make a prediction about the average annual precipitation and temperature of each city, based on the climate zone, latitude, and nearby ocean surface currents. Explain your predictions based on these factors.

Part 2: Creating Climographs

1. Select two of the cities you mapped that have similar latitudes, and find the climate information for each city on the Climate Data Fact Sheet.

2. Fill in the name and latitude of each city on a copy of the Climograph Template. Use a separate climograph for each city.

3. For each city, indicate the average precipitation for each month on that city's climograph. To do this, color in the squares above that month to the appropriate level. Refer to the precipitation values on the right side of the *y*-axis of the climograph. This will result in a bar graph of average monthly precipitation.

4. For each city, indicate the average temperature for each month by placing a dot on the appropriate line above that month. Refer to the temperature values on the left side of the *y*-axis. Connect the dots with a line to form a line graph of average monthly temperatures.

Reflect and Apply

1. Compare the average monthly temperature and precipitation on the climographs you created to your predictions. Did the data and patterns match your predictions? Why or why not?

2. What were the similarities between the climates of the two cities you compared? What were the differences? Did you expect to see these similarities and differences? Why or why not?

3. Compare your climographs to those of students who used data from different cities. Is there a pattern to the temperature and precipitation differences between inland and coastal cities? What patterns can you identify when looking at the temperature and precipitation of a coastal city that is close to a particular type of ocean current, compared to the temperature and precipitation of an inland city at the same latitude?

Extension

Find monthly average temperature and precipitation data for the location of your school or home, and create a climograph for that location.

Journal Question

How do ocean currents affect the climate of nearby areas?

In This Stage:

Your expedition goal is accomplished when you:

Can describe how clouds, the ocean, ocean currents, and cities affect climate.

Know what an El Niño is and how it influences short-term climate.

Why this is important:

Understanding natural factors that modify or control climate is needed in order to understand climate variability and change.

Words to identify:

albedo, El Niño, La Niña, urban heat island

Stage 4: Climate Modifiers

You know that climate zones are defined based on an area's temperature and precipitation. Temperature is an obvious difference between a tropical climate and a polar climate. The amount, type, and seasonal variations in precipitation can also be the difference between one climate and another.

Winds can play a large part in determining an area's annual precipitation. A region often experiences winds that consistently blow in a general direction. These prevailing winds move and steer air masses over the region, often leading to the same weather patterns. Likewise, a region might experience the same seasonal winds — winds that occur in the same season — year after year. In both cases, winds might establish weather patterns that, over many years, result in a wet or dry climate.

Climate and Clouds

Clouds are the source of precipitation. Clouds can affect climate in other ways. Thick, low-altitude clouds reflect the sun's energy back into the upper atmosphere and space. By preventing solar energy from reaching Earth's surface, these clouds cool the land and ocean beneath them. The more days per year an area is covered with thick clouds, the more likely it is the area will be cooler. **Albedo** is a measure of how much sunlight is reflected from a substance on or above Earth's surface. A thick, fluffy cumulus cloud has a high albedo.

Clouds can also prevent energy from leaving the Earth system. High, thin clouds are translucent enough to allow incoming solar radiation to pass through. However, these same clouds trap heat given off by Earth's surface — energy that would otherwise escape into space. The high, thin clouds absorb the heat and re-radiate some of it back toward Earth's surface. This contributes to Earth's greenhouse effect.

Check for Understanding

- How do clouds decrease Earth's surface temperatures?
- How do clouds increase Earth's surface temperatures?

Albedo of Surfaces		
Surface	Average amount of light reflected	Average albedo
dark, wet soil	5%	0.05
light, dry soil	40%	0.40
dry sand	40%	0.40
pine forest	10%	0.10
fresh snow	95%	0.95
high, thin clouds	40%	0.40
low, thick clouds	75%	0.75

▲ The higher the albedo value, the greater the surface's ability to reflect — and not absorb — sunlight.

Effect of the Ocean on Climate

Earth's land and water do not respond to the sun's energy in the same way. The surface of the land heats up and cools down when it is exposed to solar radiation — sunlight — and it does so more quickly than the water. Even if a rocky area gets very hot during the day when the sun is shining on it, the thermal energy does not move very far into the ground. Water, however, is a fluid. When water absorbs energy from the sun, that energy can flow throughout the body of water, transferring the heat to another location.

Remember that water has a high heat capacity. That is, it takes a long time to warm up a mass of water, and once the water is warmed, it takes a long time for it to cool down. This is why large bodies of water hold more heat energy than similarly sized areas of land. The water also holds on to the thermal energy longer than land.

For all these reasons, the ocean or even large lakes such as the Great Lakes moderate the temperature of nearby land. Coastal climates are less extreme than climates farther inland, away from the ocean. Differences between day and night temperatures are less extreme next to large bodies of water, as are differences between winter and summer temperatures.

Coastal climates are also often wetter than climates farther inland. Evaporation from the ocean adds water vapor to the air. The southeastern United States is in the humid subtropical climate not only because of the temperatures in the region, but also because of the precipitation made possible by warm, moist air coming in from the Gulf of Mexico.

While we consider air masses to be the causes of weather and not climate, having the same air mass type over the same land mass, year after year, does influence a region's climate. Major wet air masses — the maritime polar and maritime tropical air masses — form over oceans and are defined by their moisture content. The maritime tropical air mass that forms over the warm waters of the Gulf of Mexico influences much of the United States east of the Rocky Mountains during the summer. The moisture it brings to the area is not only responsible for thunderstorms (weather), but also the average annual rainfall (climate) in the region.

Lake Effect

Large lakes such as the Great Lakes can also influence local climate. Have you ever heard of lake-effect snow? Parts of Indiana, Michigan, Ohio, Pennsylvania, and New York get much more snow per year than other areas at the same latitude because of the moisture picked up by cold northwesterly winds that warm as they move across the warmer water of the Great Lakes. That moisture gets deposited as snow downwind of the lakes, particularly at higher elevations. For cities like Buffalo, New York, this can mean occasional snowstorms that dump up to 2 m (6.6 ft) of snow in 48 hours.

▼ In this satellite image, it is easy to see the lake effect snow on the southeast sides of the Great Lakes.

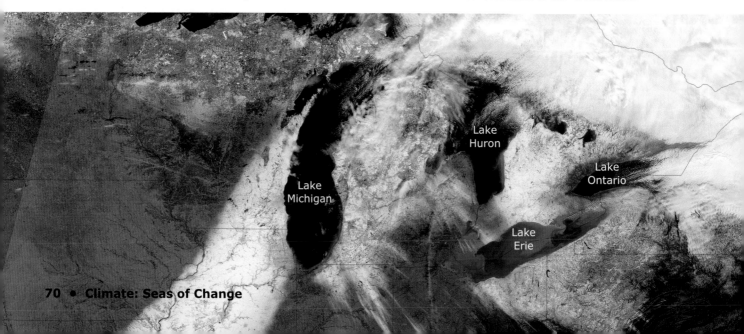

Lake Huron

Lake Ontario

Lake Michigan

Lake Erie

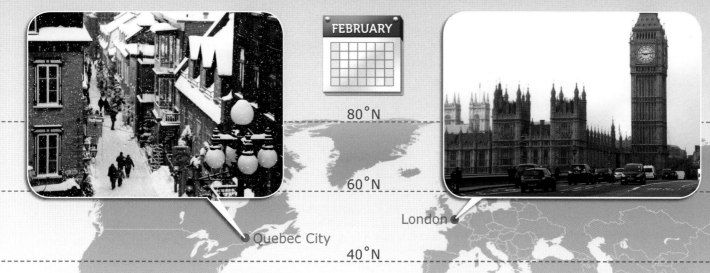

FEBRUARY

80°N

60°N

London

Quebec City

40°N

Ocean Currents and Climate

February in Quebec City, Canada, is definitely wintry. The narrow streets of Old Quebec, already covered with snow, can get another 70 cm (27.6 in.) of snow, on average, in February alone. High temperatures in the daytime average a chilly -6°C (21°F) and average nighttime lows creep down to -16°C (3°F). But what would you expect? Quebec City is located at 47°N latitude and February is the middle of winter in the Northern Hemisphere. At that latitude, it should be cold in February.

London, England, is also in the Northern Hemisphere. If you were to visit London in February, you might reasonably expect it be just as wintry as Quebec City. After all, London is located even farther north, at 51.5°N latitude. But London is not all that wintry in February. An occasional flake of snow might fall, but there is rarely any accumulation. Average high temperatures in February are a balmy 9°C (48°F). Average lows do not even get down to freezing.

The explanation for the difference between Quebec City and London has to do with London's proximity to the ocean and the location of a warm surface current. Both deep-ocean and surface currents redistribute thermal energy in Earth's ocean, which affects climate. Warm currents carry water from the low equatorial latitudes toward the poles. Other currents — the eastern boundary currents — bring cold water from high latitudes near the poles back toward the equator. The redistribution of energy happens beneath the ocean with deep-sea currents and it happens at the ocean's surface with wind-driven surface currents. Recall that these are all part of the global ocean conveyor system of currents.

London's mild winter temperatures are due to the moderating effects of the North Atlantic Current, the continuation of the warm Gulf Stream current that moves north along the east coast of the United States before crossing the Atlantic Ocean. The Gulf Stream brings warm water (and the occasional coconut shell) to coastal western Europe. The warm water warms the air above, which leads to milder-than-expected winters.

A warm current moving along a continent's coast warms the air above it, which picks up more moisture from the water. This causes a warmer and wetter coastal climate than expected. A cool current moving along a coast cools the air above it. So, the cool surface current causes a cooler and drier coastal climate than expected. For example, the cool California Current that runs south along the west coast of the United States keeps the summers cooler from Oregon to southern California than would be expected at that latitude.

Team Highlight
Diane Stanitski and the Argos watch as the second Adopt a Drifter buoy they launched drifts away from the ship. They hoped this buoy, launched south of the Channel Islands, would continue to move south into the California Current.

Technology Connection

Papa Mau

Scientists are always exploring new and different technologies for exploring the ocean. In late 2012, a wave-powered, autonomous robot glider completed a 14,500 km (9,000 mi) trip across the Pacific Ocean. "Papa Mau" spent more than a year at sea, traveling at a speed of about 3 km/h (2/mph). Its sensors recorded a single phytoplankton bloom along the equator that was over 1,930 km (1,200 mi) wide. Combined with satellite imagery, this new form of "swimming" data collection device should allow scientists to more accurately model ocean processes affecting climate.

El Niño and La Niña

Ocean and wind currents are typically constant; their effects on climate are fairly predictable. Take the Pacific Ocean, for example. Normally, near the equator in the Pacific, the air pressure in the western Pacific is lower than in the eastern Pacific, and strong trade winds blow from east to west. These trade winds push warm surface water to the west toward Indonesia and Australia. Water temperatures in the western Pacific are about 8°C (14°F) higher than water tempuratures at the same latitude in the eastern Pacific. As warm water moves west, upwelling occurs along the western coasts of North and South America, drawing deep, nutrient-rich cold water to the surface.

However, approximately every three to four years, a change occurs. The air pressure in the tropical Pacific swings, and the pressure becomes lower in the eastern Pacific than in the western Pacific. The trade winds weaken and, at times, even reverse direction. The absence of strong trade winds allows the warm surface water to flow from the western Pacific Ocean back toward the eastern Pacific Ocean. The upwelling in the eastern Pacific decreases or stops. This warm phase — characterized in part by the flow of unusually warm surface water from the western Pacific Ocean toward the west coast of South America — is known as **El Niño**.

Often a cold phase known as **La Niña** occurs just after El Niño. During La Niña, there are unusually low pressures in the western Pacific Ocean and higher pressures in the eastern Pacific Ocean. The pressure differences cause stronger-than-normal easterly winds to blow across the Pacific Ocean. The winds result in

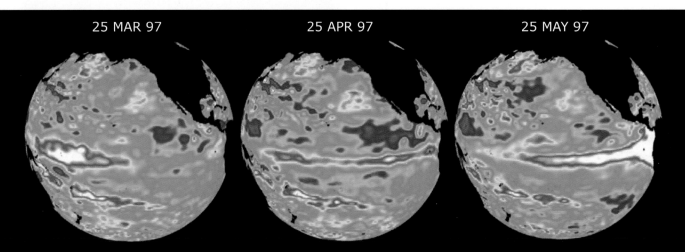

| 25 MAR 97 | 25 APR 97 | 25 MAY 97 |

These three views of the Pacific Ocean show changes in sea-surface height from a developing El Niño. The white and red areas have higher-than-normal sea surface height and also represent a warm water mass moving east across the Pacific.

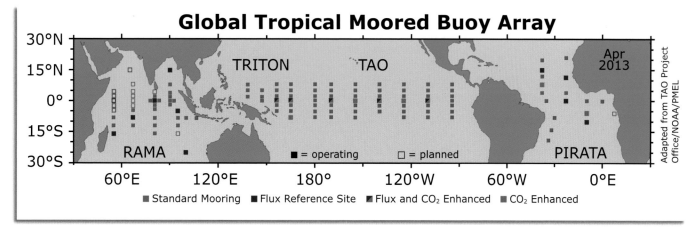

Global Tropical Moored Buoy Array

30°N

15°N

TRITON   TAO

Apr 2013

0°

15°S

RAMA   ■ = operating   □ = planned   PIRATA

30°S

60°E   120°E   180°   120°W   60°W   0°E

■ Standard Mooring   ■ Flux Reference Site   ■ Flux and CO_2 Enhanced   ■ CO_2 Enhanced

Adapted from TAO Project Office/NOAA/PMEL

▲ The Global Tropical Moored Buoy Array includes moored buoys in the Indian, Pacific, and Atlantic Oceans.

Fast Fact

The full name for the El Niño/La Niña pattern is the El Niño-Southern Oscillation, or ENSO. Scientists comparing data from the eastern and western South Pacific Ocean had noticed that there was a back-and-forth shifting of air pressure. They called this the Southern Oscillation. It was not until the 1950s that scientists realized that El Niño and the Southern Oscillation were part of the same event.

more intense upwelling in the eastern Pacific Ocean, which in turn causes colder-than-normal sea surface temperatures in the tropical eastern and central Pacific Ocean.

What short-term climate changes are brought on by El Niño? El Niño affects climate by modifying the normal temperatures and precipitation in many areas of the world. During an El Niño year — a year in which there is an El Niño — the flow of warm surface waters builds up in the eastern Pacific Ocean. Moisture from the warm water gets carried over land, leading to heavier-than-normal precipitation in Peru. The northern United States experiences warmer-than-normal winters and the southeastern United States receives more precipitation. Other areas, such as eastern Australia, are much drier than normal and can experience severe brush fires. Western Pacific nations experience drought, which can lead to food shortages.

Like El Niño, La Niña brings short-term climate changes. In La Niña years, the Pacific Northwest and northern central areas of the continental United States experience colder-than-normal

winters. The southern United States is drier than normal and may experience droughts. At the same time, parts of Asia experience heavier-than-normal precipitation that can result in flooding.

El Niño and La Niña events cannot be prevented, but they can be predicted. One of the buoy networks Diane Stanitski gathers data from is the TAO/TRITON array of moored buoys. A moored buoy is anchored to the bottom of the ocean, sometimes on a cable that is 5 km (3 mi) in length! Unlike a drifting buoy, a moored buoy is meant to stay in one location. The TAO/TRITON array contains approximately 70 buoys positioned along and near the equator, across the width of the Pacific Ocean. The buoys gather real-time data and measure humidity, wind, air pressure, wind speed and direction, precipitation, air temperature, sea surface and subsurface temperatures, and salinity. At some locations, the buoys also collect information on ocean currents and the exchange of carbon dioxide between the air and water. Data from these buoys are fed into computer models that can predict the development of El Niño and La Niña events one to three seasons in advance. This information can help people in affected areas be better prepared for climate-related variability in temperature and precipitation patterns.

Check for Understanding

- Describe how a warm surface current affects nearby coastal climates.

- What is the effect of an El Niño on the coast of South America?

Effects of Land on Climate

You already know that the continents deflect deep-ocean currents as well as surface currents, both of which affect Earth's climate. What other effects do you think land has on climate?

One place to start is with albedo. Snow and ice have high albedo values. They reflect a large amount of incoming light. There is less solar energy absorbed and transferred to the air above by land covered by ice and snow. On the other hand, dark soil and dark, leafy trees do not reflect much light; they have a low albedo. The air over darker land is more likely to heat up as solar energy is absorbed by the land and then transferred to the air above.

The elevation and shape of the land's surface can affect winds, which can then affect climate. If the land's surface is flat, winds can whip across it without being slowed down or redirected. But most land is not flat, and the large and small bumps on Earth's surface affect how winds move.

Think back to the different climate zones. What makes the highlands climate different from other climates or even the surrounding climate? The highlands climate occurs on mountains. Air temperature decreases about 6.5°C (11.7°F) for every 1 km (0.6 mi) increase in elevation. A mountain that is high enough — even one located at Earth's equator — is still cold at the top. Mount Kilimanjaro in Africa is a good example. It is near the equator yet supports glaciers at its peak.

Mountains also influence rainfall. What happens when moist air, carried along by wind, encounters a mountain or mountain range? The air cannot go through a mountain, so it starts to go over the mountain by climbing up the mountain's face. As the air rises, it cools. Condensation occurs, clouds form, and rain falls on the side of the mountain facing the source of the moist air (called the windward side). Vegetation on this side of the mountain is plentiful because water is plentiful. By the time the air moves over the mountain and then down the other side, the air has lost most of its moisture and is relatively dry. Therefore, the climate on the far side of the mountain or mountain range (called the leeward side) is drier. This dry area on the far side of the mountain is in what is called a rain shadow.

Climate can determine what type of plants can grow and where. And vegetation, in return, can affect the climate in a variety of ways. You already know that many plants have a lower albedo than light-colored soil or ice. On the one

▼ Deserts are common on the leeward sides of mountain ranges. Do you see why?

condensing water vapor

rain shadow region

moist, rising air

dry, descending air

windward   leeward

hand, the darker color of vegetation means that it absorbs energy and then radiates heat to its surroundings. On the other hand, plants also transpire, releasing water vapor into the air, which lowers nearby temperatures by a process called evaporative cooling. Finally, green plants grow via photosynthesis, adding oxygen to the atmosphere and removing carbon dioxide, which is a greenhouse gas.

Urban Effects on Climate

Annual average air temperatures in large cities can be at least 1 to 3°C (1.8 to 5.4°F) warmer than those in their rural, less developed surroundings. This is called the **urban heat island** effect. Buildings and streets are made of materials that absorb the sun's visible light during the day and re-emit thermal energy both day and night. Concrete, brick, and asphalt all have a high heat capacity, like water. It takes these materials a long time to cool down.

Try This!

Place a black square of paper and a white square of paper in strong sunlight. Try doing this at midday and when there is no wind. Place an ice cube in the middle of each square. Leave the squares in the sunlight for 20 minutes. When you return, observe the ice cubes and the paper squares. Continue to check the squares every 5 minutes until both ice cubes are completely melted. Describe any differences.

What else do you know about large cities as compared to rural areas? A city may have scattered parks or tree-lined streets, but rural locations usually have more areas of exposed soil, grass, and trees. The presence of more soil and vegetation causes rural areas to experience more cooling than cities. The tendency for urban

Compare the visible light (left) and infrared (right) images of Baton Rouge, Louisiana. Do you see that the yellow and red areas in the infrared image are roads and buildings? The cooler blues and greens are water and areas of grass and trees. The red areas are about 65°C (149°F). The dark green and blue areas are about 25°C (77°F). The Mississippi River is on the far left edge.

areas to have fewer plants also means less water is released through transpiration. Additionally, rainfall in cities runs off into storm drains rather than evaporating into the atmosphere. For all these reasons, the climate in a large city tends to be drier than the climate in the surrounding areas.

Cities also generate and release waste heat. Waste heat is heat released by a machine or an electrical appliance that is emitted to the air without being used. A car, for example, needs a radiator to keep the engine cool. The heat the car produces is wasted energy; it does nothing to help the car move. And as waste, it gets released into the environment. The more people who live and work in an urban area, the more energy gets consumed to provide temperature-controlled spaces. Energy is also used for lighting and for transportation. All of these uses of energy release waste heat that adds to the urban heat island effect.

Large cities can also affect the climate in nearby areas. During the warmer months, an urban heat island creates rising air and new patterns of wind circulation that can produce clouds. These clouds can grow and become rain-producing clouds or even storms downwind of the city. NASA scientists have used satellite instruments to explore rainfall rates near several cities in the United States, including St. Louis and Atlanta. They found 28% greater monthly rainfall rates within 30 to 60 km (18 to 36 mi) downwind of a major city compared with rainfall upwind of the city.

If humans can affect the local climate within a city, or the regional climate downwind of a city, what effects might humans have on Earth's

▲ Have you accidentally touched an incandescent light bulb when it is lit? The heat you felt was waste heat. It was an unwanted by-product of getting light from electricity. Waste heat from cars and buildings contributes to the urban heat island effect.

climates by changing the composition of Earth's atmosphere? For Diane Stanitski, John Adler, and other scientists, gathering data to answer that question is part of their daily job. What is climate change, and how can we influence its direction?

Check for Understanding
- How does the elevation of land affect the climate?
- Describe the urban heat island effect.

STEM Spotlight

Tracy Romano

Career: Biologist
Born: Rochester, NY
Education: B.A., Saint Michaels College, Winooski, VT
Ph.D., University of Rochester School of Medicine, Rochester, NY

Tracy Romano was a kid with an interest in dolphins. That interest led her to become a biologist, researching dolphin immune systems. Now, in her present job at the Mystic Aquarium in Mystic, CT, Romano oversees the aquarium's research and zoological operations. That means that Romano is in charge of the animal collection and exhibits, the animal care and research programs, and the animal rescue program. "I have an office, but I can step out of it and visit with beluga whales, sea lions, penguins, and all of our fish and invertebrates."

Romano still has time to pursue her research interests. For much of the last decade, Romano has spent several weeks each summer in the Arctic, studying the wild beluga whales of the Chukchi Sea and more recently Bristol Bay and Cunningham Inlet, in the high Canadian Arctic. "It is important to study belugas because they are an indicator species. Changing ice patterns due to climate change affect the belugas, as do changes in the abundance and distribution of what the belugas eat."

Romano has also developed a close relationship with the people of Point Lay, an Iñupiat village on the northwest coast of Alaska. "The native communities still hunt belugas for subsistence. I received permission to be on hand during sanctioned hunts to collect samples needed for my research." Students from Point Lay have traveled to Mystic as part of an educational exchange program.

Romano holds a hoop net over the head of a beluga whale near Point Lay, Alaska, as the science team attaches a satellite tag to the whale.

Q & A

What books and television shows did you like as a kid?
I liked reading Nancy Drew books because I liked trying to solve the mysteries! I also liked watching the detective show, *Columbo*. I liked watching him unravel the mystery each week, clue by clue.

Were you interested in biology from the beginning?
It was actually a first-grade teacher who inspired my interest in biology. I remember setting up a science laboratory in my basement that had my rock, shell, and birds nest collections, my map of the moon, weather station, etc. Even then I was fascinated with the dolphin brain. I wanted to know how intelligent dolphins really are.

Describe a typical day for you in your job.
My job varies from day to day. One day I may need to focus on writing a grant proposal for my research. I might work with the aquarium's exhibits team to plan a new exhibit. I may go watch a veterinary procedure on our seals. Then there are the days when we return a rescued and rehabilitated seal to the wild. That's not a typical day, but it's so rewarding when the crate door is opened and the seal goes back into the ocean.

Do you have any advice for students?
Follow your passion — do what you love. Make your own opportunities and surround yourself with the best people.

Tracking Drifting Buoys

Recall that your expedition goal is to investigate how energy flow in the Earth system creates global winds and surface currents and influences climate. Now that you have been fully briefed, it is time to put your knowledge of surface currents to work to identify an El Niño year based on data from drifting buoys.

As part of her work with NOAA, Diane Stanitski tracks drifting buoys and other data collection devices. She uses the data collected from these buoys to better understand the role the ocean plays in climate. Stanitski is interested in El Niño and La Niña events because, during these warm and cold phases of the ENSO cycle, there are strong connections between tropical Pacific conditions and weather and climate patterns across many regions of the globe (also known as "teleconnections").

In this field assignment, you will map and graph data from several drifting buoys. You will then examine the data to identify an El Niño year.

Expedition Challenge

- Plot latitude and longitude coordinates on a map to track the path taken by a drifting buoy.
- Identify surface currents that affected the course of the drifting buoy, and predict where the buoy traveled next.
- Analyze sea surface temperature data from drifting buoys over several years, and identify which year(s) were El Niño years.

Materials
- **Drifting Buoy Data Sheets**
- **computer with Internet access and Google Earth installed**
- **Global Surface Currents map (p. 56)**
- **graph paper or graphing software**

Part 1: Mapping the Data

1. Select one drifting buoy from the Drifting Buoy Data Sheets and review the date, latitude, longitude, and sea surface temperature information for your chosen buoy.

2. Open Google Earth. Plot the data for your drifting buoy on the map by following the steps below:

   a. Begin by adding a new folder. Select "Add" from the top menu and then select "Folder."

   b. When the "New Folder" window opens, enter your last name and the year of the drifting buoy you selected in the "Name" field. Click "OK."

   c. Click "Add" from the top menu and then select "Placemark."

   d. When the "New Placemark" window opens, enter the date from the first row in your data table in the "Name" field.

   e. Enter the latitude and longitude coordinates of the drifting buoy's location on that date in the "Latitude" and "Longitude" fields.

   f. In the "Description" field, enter the sea surface temperature data for that date and location.

   g. Identify the range in which the sea surface temperature falls on the Temperature Range Key on your Drifting Buoy Data Sheet. Click the "Style, Color" tab in the "New Placemark" window, and change the "Icon" color to the color for that range. Click "OK." (Note that you should not change the "Label" color, which controls the color of the text that will label the icon and should stay at the default setting of white.)

   h. In the "Places" tab to the left of the map, right-click on your folder name and select "Save Place As." (You can use control-click to get to the "Save Place As" option on a Mac.) Navigate to the place you want to save your map, and save it with the same name as your folder.

   i. Follow steps c through g to enter the rest of the data for your drifting buoy.

   j. Review the data on your map to make sure everything is accurate. If you need to make a change and are working on a PC, right-click the pin icon you would like to edit, and select "Properties." If you are working on a Mac, control-click the pin icon and select "Get Info." This will open the "Edit Placemark" box where you can make any changes. Click "OK" to save your changes.

Part 2: Making Observations

1. In Google Earth, zoom out to see where your place markers are in relation to the ocean and continents.

   a. In what part of the ocean are the place markers located?

   b. What is the closest continent? Describe the location of the place markers in relation to that continent (northwest, southeast, etc.).

2. Zoom in until you can make out the individual place markers, but do not zoom so far that you can no longer see all of your place markers.

   a. In which direction did the buoy move?

   b. Does it seem that the buoy moved at a steady pace? Explain your response.

3. Look at the Global Surface Currents map (p. 56). Compare the map to the path of the drifter you tracked in Google Earth.

   a. Which current (or currents) do you think carried the drifting buoy? Explain your reasoning.

   b. Is this a warm or cold current? Explain your reasoning.

   c. Predict where the drifting buoy traveled next. Explain your reasoning.

Expedition Debrief

1. Compare the maps of buoy data from September for each year between 1993 and 1998. Use the method your teacher indicates to gather a complete set of buoy data maps.

   a. Identify the outer boundaries in latitude and longitude of the entire set of data from all maps in your set.

   b. Identify the temperature range of the entire set of data from all maps in your set.

2. Use the color-coded place markers to compare the temperatures in September of each year.

   a. What do you notice about the temperatures in general?

   b. Do you notice any data that seem unusual?

   c. Based on these data, in which year(s) do you think an El Niño event took place?

3. Mapping is one way to visualize data. Another way to visualize data is through graphing. Create a graph of the data in your set to help you better visualize differences in temperature from year to year. Before you begin your graph, consider the following:

   a. What type of graph is best suited for displaying real data over time?

   b. What is the range of dates for your data? What is the best way to divide this range?

   c. What is the range of temperatures for your data? What is the best way to divide this range?

   d. How would your graph look different if you were to start the temperature scale with 0°C and use intervals of 5°C as opposed to starting the scale with the lowest temperature in the range and using intervals of 1°C? Which graph would make it easier to see smaller variations in temperature?

4. Look closely at your graph.

   a. Lightly draw in lines showing what you think might be the "normal" range of the temperatures. Note any temperatures that fall outside this range.

   b. Based on your graph, in which year(s) do you think an El Niño event took place? Is this the same year or years you identified based on the Google Earth data?

   c. Do you notice any other data that seem outside the normal range? What might explain these data?

   d. Was it easier for you to visualize the data in the map format or the graph format? Why?

Journal Question

How confident are you in the conclusion you drew from the available data? Why? How could you increase your confidence in identifying an El Niño event?

Expedition 3

Climate Change
Models and Decisions

"If you stop everything right now as it is, humans have already had a long-lasting impact on Earth's climate. But students can play a role in mitigating additional impacts on climate change and the challenges faced by future generations."
—Dr. James J. Hack
Director, National Center for Computational Sciences
Oak Ridge National Laboratory

Jim Hack

In his job at Oak Ridge National Laboratory (ORNL), Jim Hack is in a unique place. He not only helps refine climate change models, but also gets to see those models run on some of the world's fastest supercomputers.

Meet the Researcher Video
Come meet Jim Hack in the Oak Ridge National Laboratory's arboretum. How did a tenth grader with an interest in weather become an expert on climate change and the man in charge of the ORNL supercomputers?

Read more about Jim Hack on the JASON website.

Your Expedition Goal...

Investigate the causes and impacts of climate change and learn how scientists are working to predict Earth's climate future.

To accomplish your goal successfully, you will need to:

- Discuss natural factors that cause climate change, such as the effects of clouds and variations in Earth's position and orientation in space.
- Describe ways in which humans are the primary cause of global warming.
- List and describe the effects of continued global warming.
- Explain how scientists construct and use computer climate models.
- Describe global, local, and personal efforts to reduce the amount of greenhouse gases released into Earth's atmosphere.

Join the Team

Jim Hack gives Argonauts (L to R) Karthik Uppaluri, Dean Taylor, Kate Burnett, and Melinda Woods-Carpenter a tour of ORNL's computer visualization chamber known as EVEREST (Exploratory Visualization Environment for Research in Science and Technology).

Hot Topic

"Yes, it's happening. Right now."

Jim Hack has no doubt Earth is warming. That is only one of many things about climate change that Hack and other climate scientists now understand from years of gathering data, creating climate models, and then running the models on supercomputers. That does not mean Hack is never surprised by results of a particular simulation. It was a surprise that when the team ran the models using a smaller horizontal scale, hurricanes appeared in the simulations at the right time of year and in their expected locations. The model created hurricanes where none existed, based simply on the mathematics of the models!

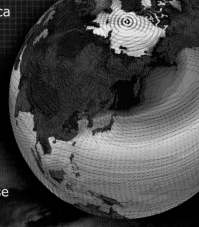

Think about Earth as you know it. You know Greenland and Antarctica are covered in glaciers, and the North Pole is white with sea ice. You know that the climate in the American Midwest is good for growing crops. In the Carolinas, winters are mild and summers are hot and sticky. But what if all that changes? What if the ice covering Greenland keeps melting? What if it gets too hot or too dry to grow crops in the Midwest? It is important to understand how and why climate is changing. But how do scientists even know that Earth is warming?

The work of climate scientists is far from done. There are new discoveries about Earth's changing climate to be made as new data sets become available and as global climate models are tweaked and refined. Would you like to use the world's fastest computer? With so much at stake, we could use more climate scientists like Jim Hack.

Expedition 1 Briefing Video
Prepare for your expedition by viewing this video clip. Learn how Jim Hack and other scientists use computer models to understand Earth's climate past and predict its climate future.

In This Stage:

Your expedition goal is accomplished when you:
Know and can describe the natural causes of climate change.

Can explain why Earth's ice ages occur in cycles.

Why this is important:
Understanding the natural causes of climate change allows us to more clearly identify and understand the impact of human-linked causes of climate change.

Words to identify:
sunspots, ice age, glacial, interglacial, eccentricity, perihelion, precession

Stage 1: Clouds, Ice, and Smoke

You only have to take a few trips around New England with a geologist to understand that Earth has undergone climate changes in its past. The signs of a great continental glacier are everywhere. Large granite boulders the size of a house — glacial erratics — are scattered about, torn off mountains hundreds of kilometers to the north in Canada. Even Plymouth Rock came from the north — perhaps from Canada or Cape Anne. Small teardrop-shaped hills called drumlins scatter the countryside. Small kettle ponds, such as Walden Pond, formed when blocks of ice melted and left holes in the glacial sediment in front of the retreating ice. Even Cape Cod is glacial, representing a place where the great ice sheet stopped for a time, neither moving forward nor backward, instead just melting and dumping its embedded load of boulders and cobbles.

Of course, you will not find a continental glacier in New England today. The climate has changed since the days of the wooly mammoth.

▲ Woman standing next to a glacial erratic in Vermont

And, unlike the global warming that is melting today's ice sheets in Greenland, this change in climate was not caused by humans. Some climate change occurs naturally.

Natural Causes of Climate Change

When it comes to Earth's climate, the sun starts it all. Both weather and climate are determined by the energy that reaches Earth from the sun each day, year after year and century after century. Solar energy drives the winds and the ocean currents. It heats our air and water. It is safe to assume that, if the sun released less energy, Earth would experience colder climates. If the sun released more energy, our climates would be warmer. Even small variations in the sun's energy output could lead to large differences in Earth's climates.

The sun actually does experience both short-term and long-term variations in its energy output. Since 1978, scientists have been able to use satellites to take direct measurements of energy reaching Earth from the sun. Scientists must use indirect methods to estimate variations in solar energy output for times before 1978. Tree rings, ice cores, and fossil pollen can all be used to provide indirect evidence of changes in the sun's energy output and its effect on Earth's climate.

Sunspots and Sun Cycles

Another indirect way that scientists estimate variations in the sun's energy output is to examine historical records of sunspot activity going back several hundred years. **Sunspots** are darker, cooler areas on the surface of the sun. You might think that, if sunspots are cooler, the sun must give off less energy when there are many sunspots. The opposite is true. Sunspots occur when the sun is most active.

Every 11 years or so, more energy is released by the sun — and reaches Earth — when the sunspot cycle reaches its peak. During a peak, astronomers may observe between 100 and 200 sunspots during their daily count. That compares with ten or fewer sunspots observed in the short lull between cycles.

Are variations in the sun's energy output enough to change Earth's climate? Look at the "Little Ice Age" for example. Between the years 1550 and 1850 AD, winter temperatures in Europe were colder than normal. Snows were heavy and mountain glaciers grew and advanced. During one period in the middle of the Little Ice Age, astronomers observed only about 50 sunspots in 30 years. It was as if the sun's normal, 11-year sunspot cycles had shut down. The lack of sunspots tells us that the sun's energy output was unusually low during that time.

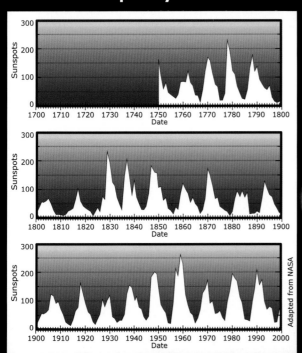

Adapted from NASA

▲ These graphs show the numbers of sunspots for the period 1750 to 2000. Can you see the 11-year cycle?

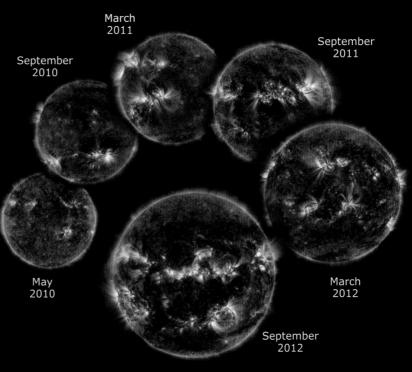

◤ In these images of the sun taken by NASA's Solar Dynamics Observatory, you can see the increase in solar activity as the sun builds up to the peak of an 11-year sunspot cycle in mid-2013.

Since 1978, scientists know from satellite data that there has been no increase in the amount of solar radiation reaching Earth. At the same time, Earth's average global temperature has continued to climb. This suggests that today's global warming must be caused by something other than increased energy from the sun.

Earth's Ice Ages

When you hear the term "**ice age**," you might think of it as one specific interval of time. But Earth has experienced five known ice ages — times when Earth's surface has been partly covered with enormous, thick sheets of ice. We are actually still in the latest of those ice ages, the Quaternary Ice Age. If we were not still in an ice age, there would be no ice sheets in Greenland and Antarctica.

Within an ice age are smaller cold and warm periods. The longer, colder times when ice sheets advance are called glacial periods or simply **glacials**. Glacials last approximately 100,000 years. These glacials are separated by shorter, warmer times called **interglacials** that last approximately 10,000 years. The average temperature during an interglacial is 4 to 6°C (7 to 11°F) higher than during a glacial. The most recent glacial period ended about 10,000 years ago. We are currently experiencing an interglacial. Since interglacials last an average of only 10,000 years, Earth should be expecting another glacial advance — if global warming does not get in the way.

When researchers looked at the timing of glacial and interglacial periods, they noticed that glacials occur in a cycle that averages 100,000 years between glacial events. (The actual time between glacials is either 80,000 or 120,000 years.) Where do these numbers come from?

Fast Fact

One of Earth's ice ages occurred in its very distant past (850 to 635 million years ago) and may have actually turned Earth into a giant ice ball. Not only was land covered in ice sheets from the poles to the equator, but some scientists believe the ocean's surface was entirely frozen over as well!

What, if anything, controls the glacial/interglacial cycle? The answer lies in Earth itself — the shape of its orbit, changes in the way its axis tilts, and how it revolves around the sun.

The shape of Earth's orbit changes from more circular to more oval and then back again. This change happens in a cycle lasting 100,000 years. The noncircular shape of Earth's orbit is referred to as eccentricity. By itself, the difference in solar energy reaching Earth due to changes in orbital **eccentricity** is too small to cause glacial events.

Earth's axis is not perpendicular to its orbital plane. The axis tilts at an angle of about 23.5 degrees. This tilt — the way the Southern or Northern Hemisphere gets more solar radiation at any given time than the other hemisphere — is why we have seasons. But it turns out that Earth's axis does not always tilt at the same angle. The angle varies from 22.5 to 24 degrees. The average amount of summer solar radiation in the higher latitudes is greatest when the tilt is greatest. The greatest tilt occurs every 40,000 years. That is not the 100,000 years average interval between glacials, but 40,000 is a factor of both 80,000 and 120,000 years.

Scientists also refer to a "wobble" of Earth in its orbit. The point in Earth's oval orbit when it

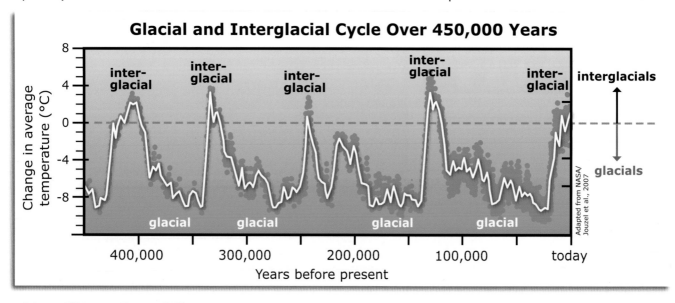

Glacial and Interglacial Cycle Over 450,000 Years

Adapted from NASA/Jouzel et al., 2007

is closest to the sun is called the **perihelion**. Today, perihelion occurs in January. In the Northern Hemisphere, cold winter weather in January is caused by Earth's northern axis pointing away from the sun. But because that happens when Earth is at its closest distance to the sun in its orbit, our winter is milder than it could be. In 11,000 years, perihelion will occur in July. Winters and summers will be more extreme. This change in when the perihelion occurs is called **precession** and occurs in 20,000-year cycles.

All of these factors — the shape of Earth's orbit, the changes in the way Earth's axis tilts, and how Earth revolves around the sun — combine to affect the amount of solar energy reaching Earth or parts of Earth. It is a combination of these factors that most likely causes Earth's ice ages, glacials, and interglacials.

What happens when the amount of solar energy reaching Earth decreases? All of a winter's snow might not melt in a cooler-than-normal summer. The snow and ice would still be there the next winter, when new snow would fall. Over hundreds or thousands of years, the thickening layer of snow could become the large, advancing ice sheets of an ice age.

Particles and Light

You have seen how changes in the amount of solar energy reaching Earth — even small changes — can affect Earth's climate. What if the amount of solar energy making it through the atmosphere to Earth's surface were to change instead? That is exactly what happens when there are tiny particles suspended in Earth's atmosphere. These particles absorb some of the sun's energy and reflect some of the energy back into space. Less energy gets through to Earth's surface, leading to lower temperatures and colder climates.

Volcanic eruptions can be a source of light-reflecting particles in the atmosphere. Think about what happens when a volcano erupts. Clouds of smoke and ash pour out of a volcano, sometimes for weeks or years. More explosive eruptions, such as the Mount Pinatubo eruption in the Philippines in 1991, throw millions of tons of sulfur-rich gases, carbon dioxide, water vapor, and volcanic dust into the atmosphere.

The 1991 eruption of Mount Pinatubo is thought to have affected Northern Hemisphere temperatures for three years following the eruption.

The 1815 eruption of Tambora is thought to be the largest volcanic eruption in modern history. The eruption may have ejected 50 km³ (12 mi³) of ash and dust and 180 billion kg (400 billion lb) of sulfur dioxide into the atmosphere. Did the eruption have an effect on climate? The next year, 1816, was known as "the year without a summer." Snow fell in Boston in June. There was ice on lakes in Pennsylvania in July and August. Crops failed in England, Ireland, and Germany, causing a famine that killed over 60,000 people.

In terms of affecting climate, the sulfur-rich gases are the main problem with volcanic eruptions. They get into the stratosphere, some 10 to 50 km (6.2 to 31 mi) above Earth's surface, where they combine with water, dust, and solar radiation to form tiny volcanic smog droplets that take months to leave the atmosphere. Once in the stratosphere, these droplets spread out, lowering the amount of incoming solar radiation over much of the planet and lowering Earth's temperature for a year or more.

A large asteroid or comet striking Earth's surface would be another source of dust in Earth's atmosphere. This type of event has probably happened several times in Earth's history. One such impact happened about 65 million years ago. Scientists have identified the impact crater buried beneath Mexico's Yucatán Peninsula. They have found evidence of dust from the asteroid or comet in sedimentary rocks of that age, all over the world. How much light would have been blocked by the dust from such an impact? One theory for the extinction of dinosaurs is that the asteroid or comet that struck Earth 65 million years ago threw so much dust into the atmosphere that it caused a mass reduction in Earth's green plants. The reduction in plants at the base of the food chain led to mass extinctions.

Dust from a dust storm can also reflect solar radiation back into space. The Saharan Air Layer is a dry, warm layer of air found over the Atlantic Ocean. When a large dust and sand storm occurs in the Sahara Desert in northern Africa, some 20% of that dust can blow out over the Atlantic Ocean within the Saharan Air Layer. Much of the dust falls out of the sky or is washed out with precipitation. But some of it stays in the air, all the way across the Atlantic. The haze from this dust layer reflects solar radiation, lowering the temperature of the water below, if only slightly. Lower water temperature may suppress the development of tropical storms.

▲ Any dust that stays in the air from this Texas dust storm could reflect solar radiation back into space.

▼ The Chicxulub crater in Mexico is estimated to be 170 to 300 km (106 to 186 mi) in diameter. Was this asteroid or comet impact the dinosaur killer?

Permian
250 million years ago

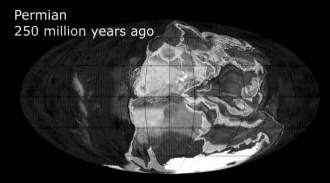

Triassic
200 million years ago

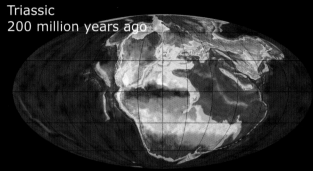

Jurassic
145 million years ago

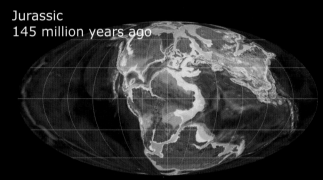

Cretaceous
65 million years ago

Present Day

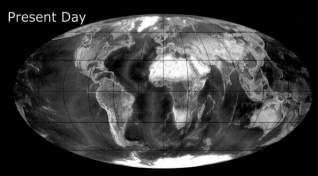

▲ During the Cretaceous period, Australia had a cool, wet climate and cold, dark winters. Can you see why?

Effects of Plate Movement

The continents that we know today have not always looked the same. They have been located at different latitudes, turned in different orientations, and joined to other land masses that we may or may not recognize as other modern continents. Earth's tectonic plates move slowly — at an average rate of 2 to 7 cm (1 to 3 in.) per year. But even slow motion can add up to great distances when that motion continues over millions of years of geologic time.

When continents change locations, they can also change climate. In the Permian period, some 250 million years ago, Earth's land masses were joined together in the supercontinent, Pangaea. Pangaea was so large that most of the land area was located far from the ocean, leaving the supercontinent's interior dry. During that time, the early reptiles — before the dinosaurs — experienced harsher winters and summers than you see today.

Plate movements have also changed the configuration of Earth's ocean. Today, the Atlantic Ocean is growing wider as plates move apart along the Mid-Atlantic Ridge, and new ocean floor crust forms. On the other side of the world, the Pacific Ocean is shrinking as plates disappear into deep-ocean trenches, subducting beneath adjacent plates. The orientation of the changing continental margins, the topography of the seafloor, the breaking apart of continents, and the creation of new seas all contribute to changes in how surface and deep-ocean currents move thermal energy within the Earth system.

Take the global ocean conveyor, for example. That system of currents was not possible before 5 million years ago when the North American, South American, and Caribbean plates came together enough to form the Isthmus of Panama. When North America became joined to South America, it cut off direct circulation of surface water from the Pacific Ocean into the Atlantic Ocean. Water evaporated in the tropical Atlantic, making the remaining water saltier. The water that evaporated was carried west as water vapor, across the Isthmus, and fell as freshwater rain over the Pacific Ocean, lowering that water's salinity. The Gulf Stream developed in the Atlantic, carrying warm, salty water north to the Arctic, where it cooled and sank. This was the beginning of the global ocean conveyor.

Clouds and Ice

Clouds also reflect incoming solar energy. Remember that albedo is a measure of the reflectivity of a surface. The albedo of clouds varies, depending on cloud droplet sizes, whether there is liquid water or ice in the cloud, the thickness of the cloud, and the angle at which solar radiation strikes the cloud from above. A cloud can reflect anywhere from less than 10% to more than 90% of incoming energy. Low, thick clouds are better at reflecting the sun's shortwave radiation — the visible light. High, thin clouds allow more incoming shortwave radiation to pass through. The shortwave radiation that is absorbed by Earth's surface is converted to thermal energy and re-emitted into the atmosphere as longwave radiation. The longwave radiation warms the lower atmosphere. Both types of clouds allow some of the longwave radiation to escape into space, but also trap some longwave radiation and radiate it back.

The total global cloud cover varies from month to month and year to year. For example, the observed global cloud cover has varied from a maximum of about 69% to a minimum of about 64% over the last 40 years. The more clouds there are to reflect solar radiation back into space, the lower Earth's atmosphere and surface temperatures will be. Even small changes in cloud cover can affect temperatures below.

Clouds reflect a lot of solar radiation, but bright, white ice and snow can reflect even more. Fresh snow has a higher albedo than a cloud. And ice, snow, and sea ice all have a much higher albedo than bare land or seawater. The greater the surface area of the ice, the more solar radiation it reflects back into space. Less energy at the surface leads to lower temperatures, which can actually lead to more snow or larger areas of ice. The reverse is also true. When ice on land or sea ice melts, lower-albedo land or water is uncovered. The newly exposed areas absorb more solar radiation and re-radiate more heat. This raises air, land, and water temperatures, which can cause additional melting.

With so many natural causes of climate change, Jim Hack and the other climate scientists would have a difficult enough challenge if their job were just to create and refine climate models to reflect the complexities of the Earth system. However, there are additional factors to add to the models — humans and the effects humans have on Earth's atmosphere.

Check for Understanding

- What are some natural causes that can lower temperatures on Earth?
- What are some natural causes that can raise temperatures on Earth?
- Describe the effects of particles in Earth's atmosphere on incoming solar radiation.

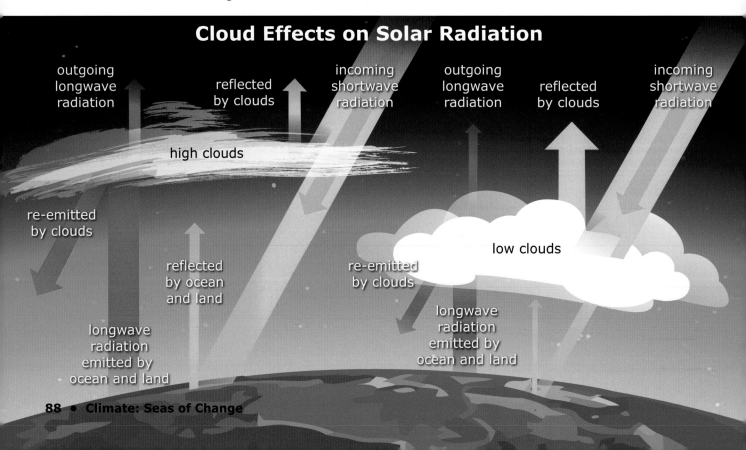

Cloud Effects on Solar Radiation

outgoing longwave radiation

reflected by clouds

incoming shortwave radiation

outgoing longwave radiation

reflected by clouds

incoming shortwave radiation

high clouds

re-emitted by clouds

low clouds

reflected by ocean and land

re-emitted by clouds

longwave radiation emitted by ocean and land

longwave radiation emitted by ocean and land

Investigating Albedo

For Jim Hack and other scientists who create climate computer models, albedo is one of many important factors to consider. For example, the scientists must account for the effects of lower-albedo land that is exposed when ice melts due to rising temperatures. In this lab, you will design and conduct your own experiment to investigate the effect of color on albedo.

Materials
- thermometers
- materials in a variety of colors
- stopwatch
- direct sunlight or other heat source

Part 1: Prepare to Investigate Albedo

1. Write a definition of albedo in your own words.
2. Explain how albedo affects climate.
3. Write down any questions you have about albedo.

Part 2: Design an Experiment

1. Examine the materials of different colors provided by your teacher. Place some of the materials in direct sunlight. Use thermometers to record the temperature under, above, and around the different materials. Observe how the different materials and placements of the thermometers affect the temperature readings.

2. Look at the sample experiment and identify the different parts that are important in a scientific experiment. These include a question, hypothesis, procedure, independent variable, dependent variable, and control.

3. Write a question about the effect of color on albedo to guide your experiment. Make sure your question is one you can test with the given materials.

4. Write a hypothesis explaining what you think will happen in your experiment. A hypothesis is a prediction about the outcome of an experiment. Your hypothesis should be written as an "If..., then..." statement.

5. List the materials you will use in your experiment, and describe what you will need to do to set up your experiment.

6. Identify the independent and dependent variables for your experiment. Variables

Sample Experiment

Question: How does growing a bean plant in a mixture of topsoil and compost affect the height of the plant?

Hypothesis: If a bean sprout is planted in a mixture of topsoil and compost, then it will grow taller than if it were planted in topsoil alone.

Procedure: Plant two bean sprouts of the same type in the same type and size of container. Fill one container with topsoil, and fill the other container with a mixture of half topsoil and half compost. Place both containers beside each other in a sunny spot. Give both plants 120 mL (4 oz) water each day. Record the height of both plants every day.

Independent variable: Amount of compost in the soil mixture

Dependent variable: Height of the plant

Control: The plant grown in topsoil alone

are factors that can be changed in an experiment. The independent variable is the one thing you change on purpose during the experiment. The dependent variable is what changes in response to changes in the independent variable. The dependent variable is what you measure and record during the experiment.

7. Identify the control for your experiment. The control is the baseline for your experiment. It shows what would happen if no variables were changed.

8. Write the procedure you will follow in your experiment.

9. Create a data table to record data during your experiment. Be sure to consider all data that may help to answer your question and prove or disprove your hypothesis.

10. Show your plan for the experiment to your teacher for approval.

Part 3: Conduct Your Experiment

1. After your teacher approves your plan, conduct your experiment. Be sure to record all the data outlined in your plan.

2. Repeat your experiment at least two more times, and record data for each trial.

3. When you have finished your experiment, average the data from each of your trials.

4. Look carefully at the data averages. Find a way to display your data so they are easy to see and understand, for example, in a table or graph.

5. Review your data. Do they support your hypothesis? Why or why not?

6. Write a conclusion explaining the results of your experiment.

Reflect and Apply

1. What main factors made your hypothesis correct or incorrect?

2. If you had to do the experiment again, what would you do differently? Why?

3. Did this experiment make you think of other questions? If so, what are they?

4. What other experiments might you do to build on what you learned in this experiment?

Extension

Identify factors that could affect albedo on Earth, such as cloud cover, ground cover, and pollution. Design and conduct an experiment to investigate the effect of one of these factors.

Journal Question

Why is albedo important to consider when modeling climate change?

▼ The black lava sand of this beach in Iceland is full of icebergs from nearby glaciers. How does the albedo of the sand differ from the albedo of the icebergs?

Your expedition goal is accomplished when you:
Know and can describe ways in which humans increase the greenhouse effect and cause global warming.

List and describe the effects of increased global warming.

Why this is important:
Understanding human-linked causes of climate change and the resulting effects of increased global warming allows us to better understand the importance of taking action to reduce greenhouse gas emissions.

Words to identify:
carbon cycle, carbon source, carbon sink, global warming, fossil fuel, deforestation, feedback loop

Stage 2: A Warming World

When climate scientists such as Jim Hack create their climate models, they must be sure to include the influences of the natural causes of climate change. They need to include the possible effects of a volcanic eruption that might happen tomorrow or in a hundred years. They need to factor in increasing albedo from greater cloud cover or decreasing albedo from melting ice. But as important as it is to include all the natural causes of climate change in the climate models, Hack knows that it is also important to factor in the effects of humans on Earth's climate.

Humans Changing Earth's Atmosphere

You have seen that there are many natural causes for changes in Earth's climate. Some of these natural causes, such as the thawing events following an ice age or a glacial, even lead to times when temperatures on Earth increase. Some people have suggested that the current warming trend we are calling global warming is simply a natural warming event, similar to other warming events in Earth's lengthy geological history.

However, the warming trend we are experiencing today is unlike anything in Earth's geological record. The climate has never warmed this quickly. If there are natural causes of climate change at work, they are being masked or amplified by human activity. The greenhouse gases that humans are pumping into Earth's atmosphere are having a larger effect on Earth's climate than any of the natural causes you have learned about.

Carbon and Climate

Carbon is a key ingredient for life on Earth. The tissue of every living organism on Earth contains carbon atoms. (If you read science fiction, perhaps you have encountered the term "carbon-based life form." The writer means you, your cat, and the tree in the park down the street. You are all "carbon-based.") Carbon is in the food you eat, the fuels you burn, and the air you breathe in and breathe out.

The Natural Carbon Cycle

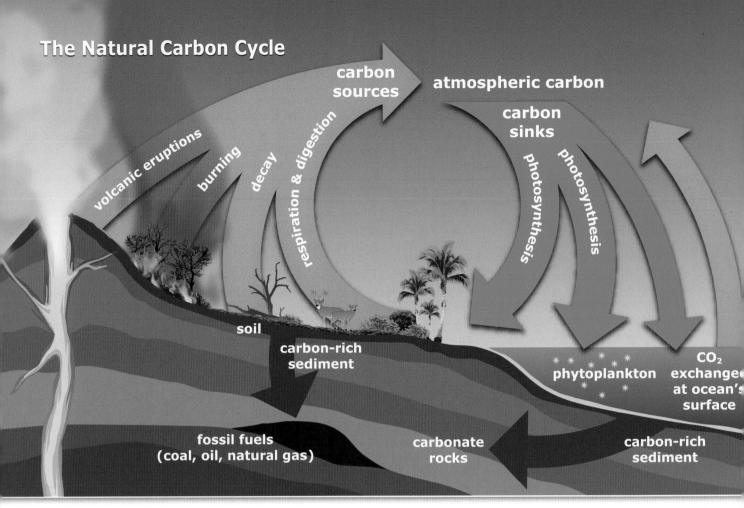

▲ Carbon is stored and released in a natural cycle. When humans burn fossil fuels for energy, they disrupt the natural cycle by releasing carbon that had been stored deep underground. The waste carbon dioxide enters Earth's atmosphere and contributes to global warming.

Earth's carbon does not stay in one place. The same carbon atoms are used and reused over time. The continuous process by which carbon is exchanged between living organisms and the environment is called the **carbon cycle**.

If you look at the carbon cycle, you can divide areas of Earth's atmosphere, land, and ocean into carbon sources and carbon sinks. A **carbon source** releases more carbon than it absorbs. A **carbon sink** is anything that absorbs more carbon than it releases. Carbon can take many different forms but is primarily moved through the carbon cycle as carbon dioxide. Carbon sources are therefore sources of carbon dioxide. Carbon sources include the burning of fossil fuels, the decay of dead organisms, and the respiration (breathing) of animals. Carbon sinks are places where carbon dioxide is removed from the cycle and carbon is stored or kept out of the cycle for a period of time. Examples of carbon sinks include living animals, organic material in soil, living or dead plants, coal and oil, limestone, the ocean, and the atmosphere.

Global Warming

Carbon is also a major factor in Earth's climate. Carbon dioxide (CO_2) and methane (CH_4) are two carbon compound gases in Earth's atmosphere. They are also greenhouse gases that contribute to Earth's greenhouse effect. Remember that when Earth's energy budget is balanced, the greenhouse effect traps just the right amount of heat near Earth's surface to keep it warm, allow for liquid water, and make the planet suitable for life.

However, if there is a greater-than-normal concentration of greenhouse gases in Earth's atmosphere, Earth's energy budget can become unbalanced. As levels of greenhouse gases, such as carbon dioxide and methane, increase in Earth's atmosphere, the natural greenhouse effect becomes greater. This leads first to an increase in atmospheric temperatures and then an increase in land and ocean temperatures. The gradual increase in air temperatures near Earth's surface is called **global warming**.

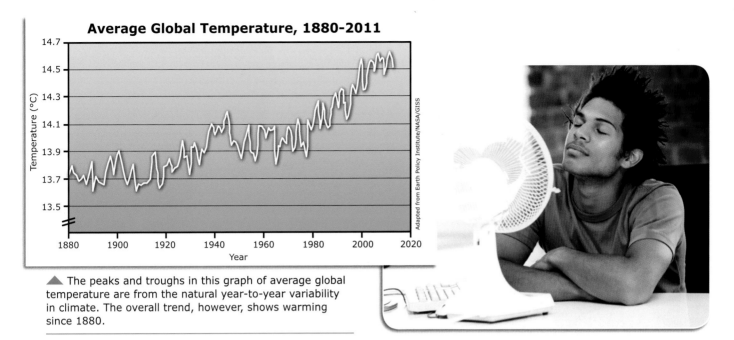

Average Global Temperature, 1880-2011

Adapted from Earth Policy Institute/NASA/GISS

▲ The peaks and troughs in this graph of average global temperature are from the natural year-to-year variability in climate. The overall trend, however, shows warming since 1880.

How do we know Earth is warming? Scientists around the world have been taking measurements of Earth's surface temperature since around 1880. As the years have gone by, the number of data stations has increased. Today temperatures are recorded at thousands of locations all over the world, both on land and at sea. These data show that Earth's average surface temperature has increased by more than 0.8°C (1.4°F) over the past 100 years. Much of that temperature increase has taken place over the past 35 years. Earth is definitely warming.

Are concentrations of greenhouse gases increasing in Earth's atmosphere? NOAA scientists at the Mauna Loa atmospheric research station in Hawai'i have been measuring and recording the amount of carbon dioxide present in the atmosphere since 1958. Their measurements show that atmospheric carbon dioxide levels have been steadily rising since the project began.

Is it possible to know the levels of carbon dioxide in Earth's atmosphere before 1958? Ice cores taken in Greenland and Antarctica provide scientists with important data. The ice cores contain annual layers of ice. Within the ice are tiny bubbles of trapped air — samples of Earth's atmosphere, thousands or even hundreds of thousands of years old. Analyses of these gas bubbles provide scientists with a way to make direct measurements of past carbon dioxide concentrations. Records from these ice cores show that before 1950, there was no time during the last 650,000 years when atmospheric carbon

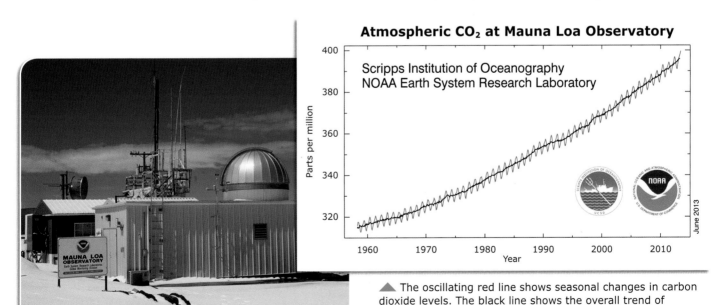

Atmospheric CO$_2$ at Mauna Loa Observatory

Scripps Institution of Oceanography
NOAA Earth System Research Laboratory

June 2013

▲ The oscillating red line shows seasonal changes in carbon dioxide levels. The black line shows the overall trend of increasing carbon dioxide concentration in Earth's atmosphere.

Researchers use data from ice cores to determine concentrations of gases in Earth's atmosphere hundreds of thousands of years ago.

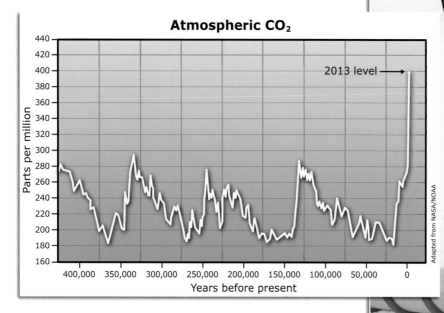

Atmospheric CO$_2$

2013 level ⟶

Parts per million

Years before present

Adapted from NASA/NOAA

▲ Based on ice-core data, scientists have documented high and low concentrations of carbon dioxide in Earth's atmosphere over the last 650,000 years. Current carbon dioxide levels are higher than at any time during that period.

dioxide concentrations were greater than 300 parts per million (ppm), not even during interglacial periods. In 2013, carbon dioxide concentrations reached 400 ppm — a level not seen on Earth in millions of years

Is the current global warming trend related to increased concentrations of greenhouse gases in Earth's atmosphere? This has not always been clear. Data from ice cores and tree rings seemed to suggest that before the incredible increase in greenhouse gas emissions by humans in the last 200 years, increases in carbon dioxide in Earth's atmosphere came after Earth's temperature began to warm, not before. More recent research seems to show that these warming events may have each started with a slight change in Earth's orbit, which increased solar radiation falling on the Northern Hemisphere. However, once the temperature started to rise, carbon dioxide in the atmosphere increased and temperatures increased even more rapidly. The extra greenhouse gases seem to have come from the ocean, the thawing of permafrost, or both. This time around, humans may have started Earth's temperatures rising by filling the atmosphere with greenhouse gases.

Check for Understanding

● What is global warming?

● Describe the observed changes in global carbon dioxide levels since 1950.

Humans and Greenhouse Gases

In order to better understand the future of Earth's climate, scientists at the Oak Ridge National Laboratory (ORNL) and elsewhere have begun to investigate how carbon moves in and out of Earth's atmosphere, ocean, and soil. While natural events and cycles can cause climate change, human activities are adding greenhouse gases to Earth's atmosphere at a rate that is also affecting Earth's climate. The observed increase of carbon dioxide in Earth's atmosphere, and corresponding increase in average global temperature, are a result of human activities such as the burning of fossil fuels, deforestation, and the abundance of livestock raised on farms.

Burning Fossil Fuels

While humans have burned coal for centuries, it has only been since the beginning of the Second Industrial Revolution in around 1870 that humans have burned fossil fuels on such a large scale. A **fossil fuel** is a natural material, such as coal, petroleum, or natural gas, which formed from the remains of living organisms in Earth's distant past and which can be burned for energy. The large-scale factories in the late 1800s were powered by coal furnaces, as were the steamships traveling the ocean. The discovery of petroleum and ways to recover it and refine it led to the popularity of the gasoline engine and more than a billion cars and trucks on Earth's roads today. Each new development of the modern age seemed to rely on the burning of more fossil fuels.

Think about the ways you burn fossil fuels each day. You may not think of it that way, of course. If you ride to school on a bus, chances are that bus burns gasoline or diesel. When you turn on a light in the kitchen or a computer, the electricity probably came from a power plant burning either coal or natural gas. Your house or apartment building is heated and cooled by energy derived from burning fossil fuels. The manufactured things you buy, from paper to plastics to mobile phones, were all made in factories that somehow, directly or indirectly, burned fossil fuels to get their energy. And when those things traveled from the factories to the stores, or from the stores to your home, they were transported in trucks or cars that burned fossil fuels.

Unfortunately, burning fossil fuels comes at a cost. When fossil fuels are burned, carbon dioxide is created as a by-product and gets released into the air. China is the world's largest source of fossil fuel-related carbon dioxide. The United States is the second largest source. The U.S. has emitted over 90 billion metric tons of carbon since 1800 from fossil-fuel consumption. As other countries in the world become more developed (have more industry, more cars, etc.), their share of global emissions will likely increase just as China's share has increased.

Fast Fact

Think of it as *CSI: Troposphere*. It turns out that carbon has a fingerprint. The carbon found in fossil fuels is millions of years old and contains very little of the radioisotope carbon-14. Carbon-14 is "new" carbon and decays over time, so it is absent in fossil fuels formed millions of years ago. When scientists look at carbon in atmospheric carbon dioxide, they find more "old" carbon and less carbon-14 than should naturally occur. Some old carbon could come from volcanic eruptions. But most of the old carbon must come from the burning of fossil fuels.

Deforestation

As plants grow, they remove carbon from the air via photosynthesis and lock carbon away in their leaves, stems, branches, and roots. When a plant dies and decays, or if the plant gets burned, some of that carbon is released back into the atmosphere as carbon dioxide or methane.

Trees are very large plants and can lock away a lot of carbon as they grow. About 50% of a tree's mass is carbon. As trees grow, they are important carbon sinks. When forests are lost through deforestation, those carbon sinks are removed. **Deforestation** is the large-scale removal of trees for farming, timber, or other land use. In South America, areas of rainforest are not only cut down, but the trees are burned to clear land for agriculture. When the trees are no longer growing, they become carbon sources. Burning the trees releases large quantities of carbon dioxide into the atmosphere, adding to global warming. Up to 30% of the greenhouse gases released into Earth's atmosphere each year may come from deforestation.

Team Highlight

At the ORNL Environmental Research Park, the Argos looked at tree roots. A surprising amount of a tree's mass — and carbon — can be locked away in its roots.

Livestock

You might not think a cow burp is much of a problem. The thought of burping cows might seem more comical than a serious cause of global warming. But there are a lot of cows (and sheep, goats, and other kinds of livestock) in the world. And they are not simply burping air. They burp methane, which is a greenhouse gas 22 times more effective than carbon dioxide at trapping heat in the atmosphere. The average large cow can release around 280 L (74 gal) of methane each day. That is enough to fill 140 2-L soda bottles! Sheep are smaller; they release only about 25 L (6.6 gal) of methane per day.

Fast Fact

A cow itself does not create the methane in its burps. The methane is formed by anaerobic bacteria in one of the cow's stomachs. Cows and sheep eat grass, which contains hard-to-digest cellulose. The bacteria help the cow digest the cellulose. Methane is an unfortunate by-product. Most of the methane gas (95%) comes out as burps. The rest comes out the other end.

How big of a problem is methane from livestock? Again, there are a lot of cows. There are about 100 million cattle in the United States alone. There are around 1.5 billion cows and sheep in the world. It is estimated that livestock produce about 80 million metric tons of methane each year. That accounts for approximately 30% of the methane entering Earth's atmosphere from human-related activities.

✓ Check for Understanding

- How does burning gasoline or natural gas contribute to global warming?

- Describe three ways that cutting down and burning a forest to make pasture for cattle can contribute to global warming.

Effects of Global Warming

Human activities have negative impacts on Earth's atmosphere in that they contribute to excess greenhouse gases that increase climate change. In terms of risk management, what are the risks of simply maintaining the status quo? The benefits of using fossil fuels and raising livestock are known. But what are the costs and effects of global warming?

Warmer Air

Global warming starts in the atmosphere. Greenhouse gases trap heat in the lower atmosphere, raising air temperatures. As you have already seen, average global air temperatures have increased by more than 0.8°C (1.4°F) since 1880. If emissions of greenhouse gases continue to rise at current rates, atmospheric carbon dioxide concentrations may be more than 850 ppm by the year 2100. That is more than double the current, record-breaking level. Climate models, such as the ones Jim Hack runs at the National Center for Computational Sciences, suggest that this level of carbon dioxide would result in an additional increase of about 3.5°C (6.3°F) in average global temperatures by 2100. This estimate may even be on the low side.

Changes in air temperature cause changes in both weather and climate. Warm air holds more water vapor. Warmer air temperatures increase evaporation from the ocean, lakes, plants, and soil. The amount of water vapor in the air increases by about 7% for every 1°C (1.8°F) of warming. Increased warming will enhance regional differences in precipitation: dry areas will get drier, and wet areas will get wetter. Scientists predict that increased warming will also generate more extreme weather, leading to stronger and more frequent storms.

Warmer Ocean

Air temperature is not the only thing that increases with global warming. In a recent study comparing ocean temperature data from the 1870s HMS *Challenger* expedition with current data from Argo drifting buoys, scientists report that average water temperatures in the upper parts of the ocean have gone up by about 0.3°C (0.6°F) over the last 100 years. Water temperatures in the tropics may have increased by double that amount. This warming has occurred from the ocean's surface down to a depth of about 700 m (2,300 ft). Because of the way water in the ocean circulates, increased temperatures will eventually affect greater ocean depths.

Warmer water is harmful to many marine organisms. Coral is one type of organism that is very vulnerable to temperature change. In coral bleaching events, reef corals lose their symbiotic algae and turn white. This bleaching slows the growth of the corals and leads to destruction of coral reefs. Not all coral bleaching events are linked to global warming; bleaching can occur due to changes in water temperature caused by El Niño, for example, or from exposure to fresh water or increased sediment. However, increased water temperature due to global warming is the most obvious threat to corals. All it takes is about a 0.5 to 1.0°C (0.9 to 1.8°F) increase in water temperature for several weeks to cause bleaching.

▼ These staghorn corals off Malaysia's Tioman Island are already undergoing bleaching due to rising seawater temperatures.

The storm surge from Hurricane Katrina caused an estimated $44 billion in property damage. The storm killed over 1,800 people.

Rising seawater temperatures also threaten other marine organisms. The small, shrimp-like organisms called krill are found at the base of many ocean food chains. As water temperatures go up, the abundance of krill goes down. A shortage of krill can starve animals that eat krill, such as penguins, seals, and whales. Predators higher up on the food chain are then affected as well.

Corals face other dangers related to increased carbon dioxide in Earth's atmosphere. The ocean is a carbon sink that helps remove carbon dioxide from the atmosphere. (Remember the carbonate buffering system?) But when the concentration of atmospheric carbon dioxide is too high, the ocean's role as a carbon sink begins to have a negative impact on marine life. Too much carbon dioxide entering the water leads to the formation of so much carbonic acid that the pH level in the ocean starts to go down. The ongoing decrease in the pH of the ocean is called ocean acidification.

Decreased pH would be bad enough, but as seawater becomes more acidic, there is a resulting decrease in the number of carbonate ions available for marine organisms that rely on calcium carbonate to form their shells or other hard parts of their bodies. As the ocean becomes more acidic, coral reef organisms are less able to build or rebuild reefs, leaving the reefs vulnerable to disease, bleaching, or destruction by storms. Some marine plankton also require carbonate ions to form their shells. These plankton are an important food source for many other marine organisms.

Warmer oceans may lead to stronger, more frequent hurricanes. Warmer surface waters more readily evaporate into the air above, adding energy and water vapor to small storms and turning them into larger, more damaging storms. Storm surges — often the deadliest and most destructive parts of a tropical storm — may happen more frequently. One study predicts that if the climate warms by just 2°C (3.6°F), large storms may occur ten times more often. That could mean a Katrina-size hurricane every other year.

Melting Ice

Global warming is also causing Earth's ice to melt. Some ice occurs as mountain glaciers. Much of it occurs as thick sheets of ice covering Greenland and Antarctica. Up until recently, sea ice covered much of Earth's Arctic area. Scientists have accurate measurements of disappearing ice. Not only can they say that Earth's ice is definitely melting, but also that the rate at which the ice is melting has tripled in the last 20 years. In West Antarctica, the annual average temperature at the Byrd research station has risen 2.4°C (4.3°F) since the 1950s. This is one of the fastest increases in temperature anywhere on Earth and is three times the global average. Warmer oceans also lead to the melting of sea ice and ice sheets from below. Large chunks of ice sheets collapse and break off, and are eventually carried into even warmer waters where the ice melts.

Melting ice is a good example of a **feedback loop**. When it comes to Earth's climate, you can think of a feedback loop as a type of circular process that either works in a way that favors climate stability (a negative feedback loop) or a way that leads to increased climate change (a positive feedback loop).

Melting ice is a positive feedback loop that tends to increase temperatures — which is not a positive thing at all. Ice has a high albedo. Much of the solar radiation that strikes ice bounces back into space without warming the land or the air above. When the ice melts, it uncovers darker colored land or water below. When solar radiation strikes those darker surfaces, the visible light is not reflected nearly as much. The light gets absorbed and changes to thermal energy that heats the land, the water, and the air above. As that land, water, and air get hotter, more ice melts, uncovering more darker surfaces, and so on.

Thawing Permafrost

Recently scientists have begun to realize the potential impact of thawing permafrost on climate change. Permafrost covers almost a quarter of the Northern Hemisphere. It is thought to contain some 1,700 trillion metric tons of frozen carbon, about twice as much carbon as contained in Earth's atmosphere.

Formed during and since the last glacial event, the permanently frozen parts of Earth's soil extend down some 700 m (2,300 ft) below the surface. Normally, only the upper 2 m (6.6 ft) of permafrost thaw each summer and then refreeze each winter. As global temperatures increase, the thickness of this thawed active layer will also increase. When that happens, the thawed permafrost will release large quantities of carbon dioxide and methane into Earth's atmosphere. The increased greenhouse gases will raise temperatures even more, causing more of the permafrost to thaw, releasing even more carbon dioxide and methane. This is another example of a positive feedback loop. Potentially, the thawing of Earth's permafrost could account for up to 39% of total greenhouse gas emissions over the next 200 years.

These melt pools are on top of the sea ice, but they still show how melting ice causes a feedback loop. Melt pools are darker than the surrounding white ice and warm more quickly.

In Arctic villages, houses and roads are sinking and cracking as permafrost thaws. Erosion and loss of sea ice also expose coastal villages to storm surges. This home on Alaska's Arctic coast was washed into the ocean when the bluff it was sitting on eroded.

Rising Sea Levels

Climate change is already causing global sea levels to rise. Over the last 100 years, the average global sea level has risen by about 10 to 25 cm (4 to 10 in.). Remember that water expands when its temperature increases. As ocean temperatures increase, the seawater expands, causing a rise in sea level. About half of the observed sea level rise over the last century has been due to thermal expansion of water. Melting of glaciers, sea ice, and the Greenland and Antarctic ice sheets have also added water to the ocean and contributed to rising sea level.

The United Nations estimates that 44% of the world's population lives within 150 km (93 mi) of the ocean. Roughly one person in ten lives in a coastal area at an elevation of 10 m (33 ft) or less above sea level. That means that two-thirds of a billion people are threatened by rising sea level. The ten countries with the most people in low-elevation coastal areas are China, India, Bangladesh, Vietnam, Indonesia, Japan, Egypt, the United States, Thailand, and the Philippines. When sea level rises, coastal areas can either completely disappear under the water or be vulnerable to flooding, shoreline erosion, and destruction from powerful storm surges accompanying coastal tropical and subtropical storms.

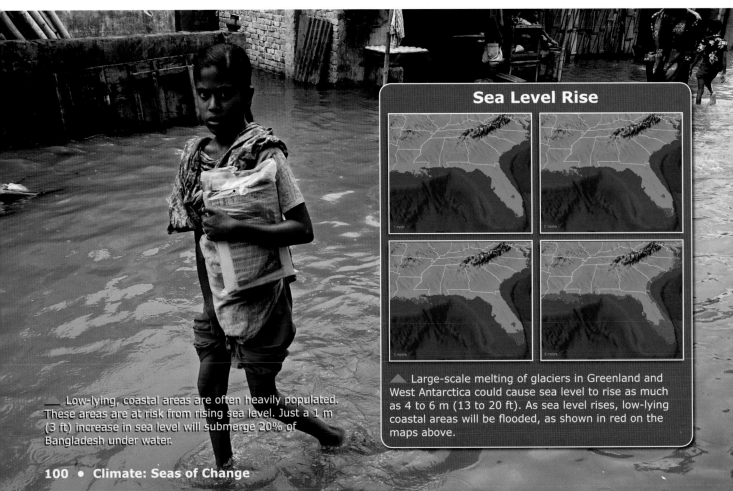

Low-lying, coastal areas are often heavily populated. These areas are at risk from rising sea level. Just a 1 m (3 ft) increase in sea level will submerge 20% of Bangladesh under water.

Sea Level Rise

Large-scale melting of glaciers in Greenland and West Antarctica could cause sea level to rise as much as 4 to 6 m (13 to 20 ft). As sea level rises, low-lying coastal areas will be flooded, as shown in red on the maps above.

Changing climates are certain to have an effect on the ecosystems found in the affected climates. Perhaps the best way to look at the potential impact of climate change on Earth's organisms is to look at a few examples of how plants and animals have already been affected.

Migration

Migration, blooming, and mating are all tied to the seasons. As temperatures have risen, the timing of these events has changed. Birds that spend their springs and summers in the Northeast have been returning from the South 13 days earlier than they did less than 100 years ago.

Growing seasons

Farmers in the Midwest might see lower crop yields due to higher summer temperatures, droughts, and increased pests. However, in other areas, higher temperatures might mean a longer growing season and more crops — or even new crops.

Range

Plant life at northern latitudes is getting greener, with plants having "moved" as much as 700 km (430 mi) north in only 30 years. Kudzu —the invasive "plant that ate the South" — has already started growing as far north as Nebraska and western Pennsylvania.

Food chains

Loss of Arctic sea ice has caused a decline in the nutrient-rich algae that once thrived below the sea ice. Those algae were eaten by plankton that were eaten by Arctic cod, which were eaten by marine mammals such as seals. Seals were eaten by polar bears that now do not have enough food.

Disappearing habitat

Penguin colonies in Antarctica are shrinking with the ice sheets. Three quarters of the colonies may disappear entirely if global temperatures climb only a couple more degrees.

With so much at stake, knowing ahead of time which changes are possible or likely would help governments plan for the effects of changing climate. Using historical climate data and mathematical formulas, researchers such as Jim Hack are able not only to create climate models that describe how different inputs affect Earth's climate, but also to simulate and predict how those inputs may have operated in the past and may operate in Earth's near future.

Check for Understanding

- Explain what a feedback loop is, and give an example of a positive feedback loop.

- In what ways does global warming threaten marine organisms like coral?

Investigating Ice Cores

Jim Hack uses supercomputers and climate models not only to forecast potential changes to Earth's climate, but also to "hindcast." By having the computers run models based on a certain starting point in the past, and comparing the results to known climate data, Hack can confirm whether the models are working accurately. One way that Hack and other scientists know what Earth's climate was like in the distant past is by examining ice cores. In Antarctica and Greenland, where the weather is so cold year-round that all precipitation falls as snow, layers of snow can build up over the years, compacting and refreezing to form ice layers. Scientists can take core samples of these layers. These cores contain accumulations of snowfalls over time, including the particles and gases found in the snowfalls. By analyzing the different layers in ice cores, scientists can gain important information about past climates. In this lab, you will make observations and collect data from simulated ice cores and use the information you gather to make inferences about the past.

Materials

- index card square, about 2.5 x 2.5 cm (1 x 1 in.)
- ruler
- white play dough
- gray play dough
- clear, jumbo straw or other coring tool
- mystery ice core
- pencil
- red colored pencil
- Lab 3.2 Data Sheet
- Lab 3.2 Information Sheet (p. 104)

Part 1: Create Ice Layers

1. Place the index card square on your desk or table. Place a layer of white play dough on top of the index card. The layer should be about 4 cm thick. This represents one summer's worth of snowfall onto the Greenland ice sheet.

2. Place a layer of gray play dough on top of the first layer. The layer should be about 1 cm thick. This represents the next winter's snowfall onto the Greenland ice sheet.

3. Add four more layers of play dough, alternating white and gray (summer and winter) layers. Keep each of the summer layers between 1 and 2 cm thick and each of the winter layers between 3 and 4 cm thick.

Part 2: Core Ice Layers

1. Press your coring tool straight down into the layers of play dough from the top. Twist the coring tool slightly to get it all the way to the bottom of the layers you created.

2. Gently remove the coring tool from the play dough.

3. Observe the ice core sample you extracted. Which layers are the oldest? Which are the newest? How do you know?

4. Identify the summer and winter layers you laid down. A summer and winter layer together represent one year of snowfall. How many years are represented in your core sample? How do you know?

Part 3: Make Observations

1. Set your play dough ice core aside and obtain a mystery ice core from your teacher.

2. Examine the mystery ice core and record your observations on the Lab 3.2 Data Sheet. Describe any patterns you see. What do you think might have caused the patterns?

3. Describe any layer that is distinctly different from the other layers in the mystery ice core. How is it different? What might have caused this layer to form?

Part 4: Collect Data

1. Measure the thickness of each layer in the mystery ice core in centimeters, and record the measurements on the Lab 3.2 Data Sheet.

2. Determine an appropriate scale, and make a scale drawing of the mystery ice core on the Ice Core Outline on the Lab 3.2 Data Sheet. Each layer in your drawing should be the same relative thickness as the corresponding layer on the mystery ice core. Use a pencil to lightly shade in darker layers.

Part 5: Interpret the Data

1. Refer to the "Annual Layers" section on the Lab 3.2 Information Sheet. Identify the summer and winter layers on the mystery ice core. Label one summer and one winter layer on your ice core drawing.

2. Refer to the "Counting Layers" section on the Lab 3.2 Information Sheet. Determine how many years are represented in the mystery ice core. Use a red colored pencil to mark each year on your ice core drawing.

3. Refer to the "Analyzing Layers" section on the Lab 3.2 Information Sheet. Find the layer with evidence of a major volcanic eruption in the mystery ice core. How many years apart is this event from the most recent year visible in the mystery ice core? Label this layer as "volcanic eruption" on your ice core drawing.

4. Refer to the "Dating Layers" section on the Lab 3.2 Information Sheet. Use the information to determine the years represented in the mystery ice core.

Reflect and Apply

1. Create a bar graph showing the thickness of the summer layers for the mystery ice core. Create a separate bar graph showing the thickness of the winter layers. Be sure to label each item with the correct year.

2. Look at the bar graphs. Which years had the thickest layers in the summer and winter? Which years had the thinnest layers in the summer and winter? What might this information tell you about the weather during those years?

3. The Industrial Revolution began in the late 1700s when people began burning coal in large amounts to power manufacturing, transportation, etc. How might evidence of the Industrial Revolution show up in ice cores?

4. Atomic bomb testing took place in the 1950s. How might evidence of nuclear tests show up in ice cores?

5. The Greenland ice cores go back 110,000 years, and the Antarctic ice cores go back over 800,000 years. What clues would looking at snowfall in ice cores over such a long period of time give you about climate change? What clues may be found in chemical analysis of the cores?

Extension

It can take hundreds of years for snowfall to freeze into ice layers that can be extracted in an ice core. To study climate for more recent years, scientists can dig snow pits. These deep pits allow scientists to look directly at the layers created by snowfall. Research snow pits and what scientists can learn about climate from studying them. Create a poster presentation to share your findings.

50 cm

100 cm

150 cm

▲ This snow pit in Antarctica is backlit with a second pit to illuminate a thin wall of snow.

 Journal Question

How can scientists use information from ice core layers to build a picture of climate over time?

Lab 3.2 Information Sheet

Annual Layers

Annual layers can be seen in the ice cores from Greenland, where there is significant snowfall. Darker layers indicate winter snowfall.

Counting Layers

In ice cores where annual layers are visible, these layers can be counted to identify how many years are represented in the ice core. Together, a summer layer and winter layer represent one year.

Analyzing Layers

Scientists can get a lot of information from analyzing the composition of gasses trapped in air bubbles in the ice. They can also get information from analyzing particulates, such as dust or ash, that are trapped in the ice. Sometimes, however, an event leaves evidence in the ice that is visible to the naked eye. For example, major volcanic eruptions can throw ash particulates high into the atmosphere. These particulates can be carried great distances through the atmosphere. Evidence of major eruptions can be found in ice cores from both Greenland and Antarctica. Volcanic ash can leave a thin, dark layer between the normal layers of ice.

▲ This 19-cm-long (7.5-in.-long) ice core section is from the Greenland Ice Sheet Project Two (GISP2) ice core. The section is from a depth of 1,855 m (6,086 ft) and is illuminated from below by a fiber optic source to show its annual layer structure. Lighter summer layers (shown with arrows) are sandwiched between darker winter layers. Can you tell how many years are represented here?

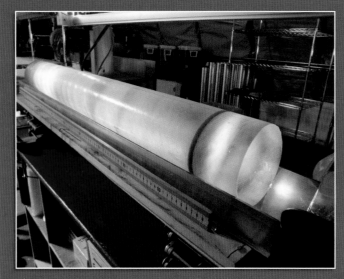

▲ The dark band in this ice core from the West Antarctic Ice Sheet Divide (WAIS Divide) is a layer of volcanic ash that settled on the ice sheet approximately 21,000 years ago.

Dating Layers

Evidence of volcanic eruptions is one way scientists are able to date the layers they are looking at in an ice core. Volcanic ash has properties unique to a specific volcano. This means that scientists can often identify the specific volcano and eruption from which the layer of ash came. By linking the ash to a known eruption, scientists can establish a date for that layer. Since evidence from a major eruption can be found around the world, scientists can also use a date they have established in one location to date layers from another location. Assume that analysis has shown the ash layer in your mystery ice core to be from an eruption that occurred in April 1815.

STEM Spotlight

Atsuhiro Muto

Career: Glaciologist and Geophysicist
Born: Oita, Japan
Education: B.S. and M.S., Chiba University, Japan
            Ph.D., University of Colorado

Atsu Muto has been interested in Antarctica since he was in middle school. So for him, being part of the 2007–2009 Norwegian-American Scientific Traverse of East Antarctica was like a dream come true. On that expedition, Muto joined six other scientists and a support crew of five in a 59-day, 2,676-km (1,663-mi) journey from a research station near the Antarctic coast almost to the South Pole. Along the way, the team set up automated weather stations and collected ice cores in hopes of establishing how quickly snow and ice accumulate in East Antarctica and whether there was evidence of human impact on climate and the ice sheet.

Not all scientists get to ride snowmobiles in blizzards as part of their job. "One upside to my job is that I get to travel a lot. Of course, having to be away from home for months at a time can be difficult." That is probably an understatement, considering the conditions a glaciologist may encounter out on the Antarctic ice — week-long storms with hurricane-force winds and temperatures below -50°C (about -60°F), drifting snow, hidden crevasses, and more. "And there's nothing like getting dropped off in the middle of nowhere by a military plane!"

Today, Muto is a research associate in the Department of Geosciences at the Pennsylvania State University. He is currently studying how the temperature in the Antarctic interior is changing, as well as how the ice-sheet flow near the Antarctic coast is affected by the rocks and ocean beneath the ice.

Muto setting up an automatic weather station in East Antarctica

Q & A

What were you like as a kid?
I was an active kid. I was always running around outdoors and playing sports.

When did you know you wanted to pursue your current career, and what drove you toward it?
In middle school I saw a piece of ice core from Antarctica. Ever since then I wanted to work in Antarctica.

What are the biggest misconceptions about your job?
People think I get to see a lot of polar animals like penguins and polar bears. I do see some, but most of the time I don't see any wildlife.

What's the coolest part of your job — other than all that ice?
Blowing stuff up! I'm a geophysicist. So I get to use explosives for some of the seismic work I do, trying to figure out the types of rocks beneath the ice or if there is any water under the ice.

What advice would you give a student interested in pursuing a career in either glaciology or geophysics?
What you are learning in school right now really is important. I get by a lot in my current job with what I learned in high school physics and math classes.

Do you have any general advice that you would like to give students?
Read a lot of books! Being a good writer helps a lot with being a scientist. Reading will enhance your writing. I didn't read enough when I was young and I regret it.

In This Stage:

Your expedition goal is accomplished when you:

Explain how scientists develop and use computer climate models.

Describe efforts being made to reduce greenhouse gas emissions and slow climate change.

Why this is important:

Understanding how climate scientists develop and validate climate models allows us to evaluate the seriousness of the climate-change threat.

Words to identify:

climate model,
carbon footprint

Stage 3: Modeling the Future

To Jim Hack, the opening of the Northwest Passage is just the sort of warning sign his computer climate models have been predicting. The Northwest Passage is a sea route connecting the North Pacific Ocean and North Atlantic Ocean, passing north of Alaska and through the interconnected waterways of northern Canada. As a trade route, the Northwest Passage has been a long-sought dream route, searched for even before it was understood that salt water could freeze. But salt water does freeze. And, up until only recently, the pack ice of the Arctic was frozen year-round and extended far enough south to block any of the possible routes.

In August 2007, satellite photos showed that Arctic sea ice had shrunk to its smallest level in the 30 years satellite photos were available. It appeared that the Northwest Passage was open. In September 2008, the first commercial ship transported cargo from Montreal to northwestern Canada via the Passage. The crew reported seeing no ice at all. The sea ice will refreeze in the Arctic winter and thaw in the summer. Soon ships traveling between Asia and Europe in the summer months may be able to avoid the Panama Canal and trim 6,400 km (4,000 mi) off their journey.

The Arctic is warming at an alarming rate. The ice sheet in Greenland is melting. The pack ice covering the Arctic Ocean is shrinking. Ice that once was thick enough to survive the summers is now thin, and the waters below are showing through at least part of the year. Less ice-covered land and sea decrease the overall albedo, increasing temperatures, melting more ice, and accelerating the warming trend via the positive feedback loop. This was something the climate models predicted. However, this is one case where the original forecast was too optimistic. It showed the acceleration of Arctic warming taking longer. Instead, the Northwest Passage could be ready for regular, summer use by commercial ships long before models had predicted.

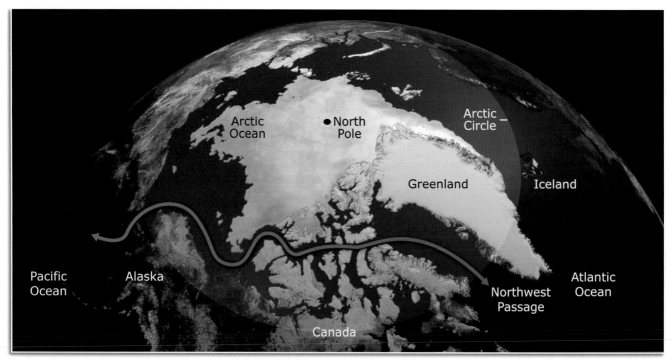

▲ As the Arctic warms and sea ice melts, ships will start to make their way through the Northwest Passage connecting the Pacific and Atlantic Oceans.

Modeling Climate Change

Climate predictions are based on data. Some data are gathered in real time at meteorological stations around the world, by satellite instruments, or by drifting buoys in the ocean. Other data are historical, based on observations made by crews on ships sailing the ocean a hundred years ago. Other historical data come from ice cores, deep-sea sediment cores, tree rings, and cave formations. All of these data can be fed into climate models. A **climate model** is a set of mathematical formulas used to describe how different variables affect Earth's climate.

Try This!

Have you heard the term "crowd sourcing"? Scientists have started crowd sourcing scientific data gathering. "Citizen science" is scientific research conducted, in whole or in part, by non-scientists. People just like you have helped look for asteroids and allowed their personal computers to run software looking for signs of intelligent life in outer space. Now there is a project where you can help provide data that can be used in predicting Earth's climate future. The Old Weather project lets non-scientists examine historic ships records from the mid-1800s to 1950. You can read and transcribe ships' logs. The data you recover can improve knowledge of past environmental conditions and can provide additional data to be fed into Jim Hack's climate models.

Jim Hack would be quick to tell you just how complicated the many variables in the climate models can be. Energy in the Earth system moves from place to place. But the energy moves at different rates in different places. Heat moves much more slowly in the ocean than in the atmosphere. This means that a climate model must take these different rates into consideration. There are also issues related to scale. The models must account for atmospheric circulation, ocean circulation, the interaction of the ocean and the atmosphere, and so on.

This is where the supercomputers at the Oak Ridge National Laboratory (ORNL) come in. Computers are particularly good at managing large amounts of data. They can do the complex calculations needed to run the models, and they can do those calculations over and over again until they reveal what the climate may look like in the future. The powerful, fast supercomputers that Jim Hack and his team use are able to run complex climate models and forecast how Earth's climate will respond to changes in atmospheric greenhouse-gas concentrations.

Checking the Model

You have seen that the climate models are very complicated. They include many different types of inputs and formulas. They need to account for sporadic events, feedback loops, and — over long enough periods of time — even sunspots and changes in Earth's orbit or axial tilt. With so much riding on our response to climate change, it is very important that scientists make these climate models as accurate as possible.

Current climate models continue to successfully predict observed outcomes in the Earth system. The models have accurately predicted the warming of different layers of Earth's atmosphere. The models have accurately predicted the way in which warming in the Arctic has accelerated. The models have accurately predicted the warming of Earth's oceans that we are observing today. The models in existence in the late 1980s predicted that a volcanic eruption would lead to a short-term cooling event of a few tenths of a degree. That prediction was proven accurate by the 1991 eruption of Mount Pinatubo. These are only a few examples of forecasts made by climate models that have had observable, accurate outcomes in the relatively short-term time scale of the last 25 years.

Running Global Climate Models

To predict changing climate requires modeling how Earth's climate functions. There are many interactions between the sun's energy and the natural processes of Earth's atmosphere, ocean, and land that affect climate. Human interactions with the Earth system also influence climate and are included in climate models.

Certain inputs are given to the model when it first runs. These include such things as geography and topography at the interfaces between land or water and the atmosphere. Another input is the amount of solar radiation at different latitudes. And then there are inputs based on human activities, such as levels of greenhouse gases and even the number of jet contrails in the sky.

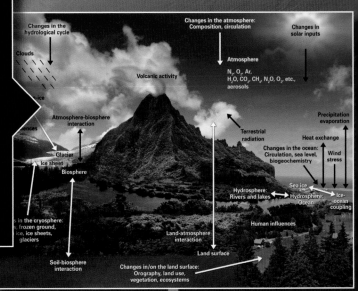

The interactions in the Earth system are stated as mathematical formulas, based on the laws of physics. All of these formulas together form the actual climate model. Complete models of Earth's climate system include processes operating in the atmosphere, ocean, land surface, and cryosphere. Depending on its complexity, a climate model can require hundreds of thousands of lines of computer code.

Conservation of momentum:

$$\frac{\partial \vec{V}}{\partial t} = -(\vec{V} \cdot \nabla)\vec{V} - \frac{1}{\rho}\nabla p - \vec{g} - 2\vec{\Omega} \times \vec{V} + \nabla \cdot (k_m \nabla \vec{V}) - \vec{F}_d$$

Conservation of energy:

$$\rho c_{\vec{v}} \frac{\partial T}{\partial t} = -\rho c_{\vec{v}}(\vec{V} \cdot \nabla)T - \nabla \cdot \vec{R} + \nabla \cdot (k_T \nabla T) + C + S$$

Conservation of mass:

$$\frac{\partial \rho}{\partial t} = -(\vec{V} \cdot \nabla)\rho - \rho(\nabla \cdot \vec{V})$$

Conservation of H_2O (vapor, liquid, solid):

$$\frac{\partial q}{\partial t} = -(\vec{V} \cdot \nabla)q + \nabla \cdot (k_q \nabla q) + S_q + E$$

Equation of state:

$$p = \rho R_d T$$

Running the climate model means applying it to a three-dimensional (3-D) map of the Earth system. Earth's surface is divided up with a grid, and the size of each cell in the grid is based on the resolution of the run. The typical case has a grid cell with an area about the size of Connecticut. At this resolution, there are about 35,000 grid cells needed to cover the entire surface of the globe. But the model does not run only along the surface; it also runs at different levels up into the atmosphere and down into the ocean. So each cell is actually a box with volume. For a model that has 20 vertical levels, there are close to a million 3-D cells to evaluate.

Each cell in the model is free to interact with the surrounding cells. The supercomputer uses the climate model equations to calculate changes to the cell over time. The amount of simulated time that is allowed to pass during a single run of a model is called a time step. For each hour, day, month, or year of simulated time, the supercomputer must run the model equations on every grid cell in the model. Then the supercomputer takes the resulting data and does the calculations all over again, moving forward in time one more step. The length of the time step and the amount of computing time depend on the model's complexity. Even the most powerful supercomputers can take thousands of hours to run a climate model that has a high resolution or that looks more than a hundred years into the future.

The data that come from running a climate model can vary depending on the focus of the model, the resolution, and other factors. Results can show changes in air temperature, precipitation, or sea-surface temperature. Climate model results are used to help scientists estimate changing sea level or variations in Earth's cloud or ice cover. Scientists analyze the results and share them with the rest of the climate-science community for comparison with results from other models.

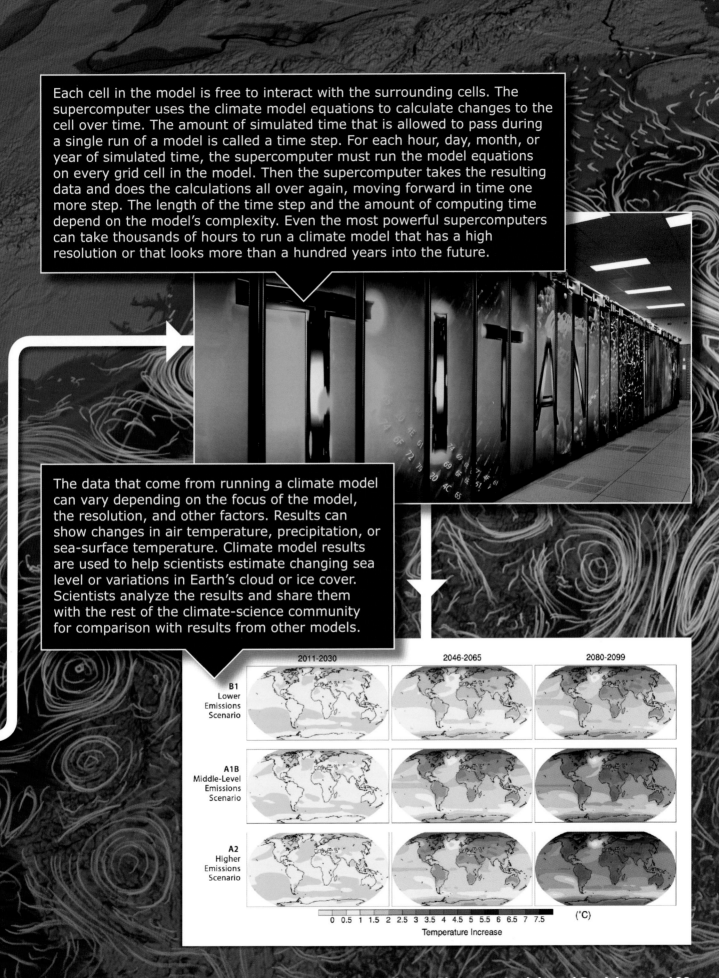

2011-2030   2046-2065   2080-2099

B1
Lower
Emissions
Scenario

A1B
Middle-Level
Emissions
Scenario

A2
Higher
Emissions
Scenario

0 0.5 1 1.5 2 2.5 3 3.5 4 4.5 5 5.5 6 6.5 7 7.5   (°C)
Temperature Increase

But climate change is something that takes place over both short- and long-term time scales. Will the changes we see today continue over the next hundred or thousand years? Will the changes continue at the same rates, or will those rates decrease or increase? Scientists need to know that their climate models are also accurate for long-term climate forecasting.

To check a climate model for accuracy over longer periods of time, Jim Hack and his colleagues use "hindcasting." Instead of starting the model with Earth's current conditions and with a starting date equal to "today," they start the model at some time in the past. The future climate they want to forecast is the one we see today. When researchers input known climate data from the past, run the model, and get output climate conditions matching those we see today, they know their model is working. The climate models Hack and his team currently use continue to pass this "hindcasting" test.

How Much, How Fast

Jim Hack and other climate scientists around the world use climate models in an attempt to predict future changes in carbon dioxide concentrations, average global temperature, and precipitation, for example. Climate models developed by different teams are run with different input assumptions to create different climate scenarios. A climate scenario is a simplified representation of the future climate that has been constructed based on differing input assumptions about how human activities might affect Earth's atmosphere and ocean. For example, one scenario might assume that humans continue their heavy use of fossil fuels, while another scenario might assume increased use of cleaner, renewable energy. Even using the same model, changing the input assumptions can change the scenario outcomes, for example, by predicting different values for the expected increase in average global temperature.

A variety of scenarios, based on 23 different climate models, have been gathered in one place by the Intergovernmental Panel on Climate Change (IPCC). The IPCC has identified several future scenarios for the amounts of atmospheric carbon dioxide over time and the predicted consequences for global temperature.

The low-growth, or "best-case," scenarios assume world population stabilizing this century and global societies moving toward cleaner fuels and less energy-hungry economies. Even these low-growth scenarios predict carbon dioxide concentrations topping 500 ppm by the year 2100. Earth's average global temperatures would still increase between 1.5 and 2.0°C (2.7 and 3.6°F) over 1990 levels.

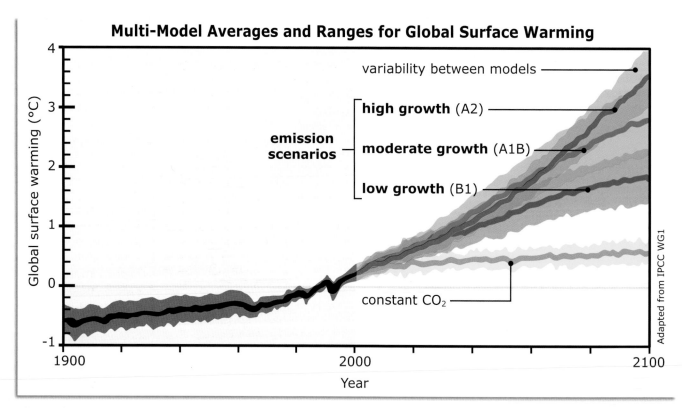

▲ Climate models show different warming rates and outcomes based on assumptions such as how much fossil fuel world economies will use in the future.

Technology Connection

EVEREST

Sometimes you need a super-sized display for your supercomputer. That is exactly why EVEREST (Exploratory Visualization Environment for Research in Science and Technology), located at the Oak Ridge National Laboratory (ORNL), was built. This state-of-the-art, super-sized data display allows scientists, engineers, and technicians to view and manipulate the data processed by ORNL's supercomputers.

EVEREST allows researchers in many scientific areas to analyze their data sets visually and in real time. Details that can be lost on smaller screens are very obvious when projected on EVEREST's giant screens. Jim Hack uses EVEREST to display some of the results from the many climate models he and his colleagues run and rerun on the giant ORNL supercomputers, named Titan, Kraken, and Gaea. Titan is the fastest computer in the world with a peak speed of 27 petaflops (27,000 trillion calculations per second). It takes that kind of calculating power to handle the complex formulas and scenarios playing out in a climate model.

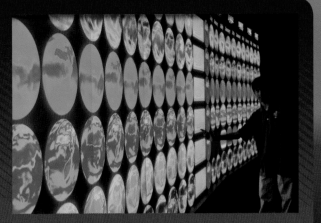

Size: 9.1 m (30 ft) wide by 2.4 m (8 ft) tall
Display Panels: Three sections with optically-enhanced glass
Projectors: 27 projectors, each capable of 2,500 lumens
Graphics Rendering: 14 desktop PC nodes connected by a gigabit network. Each PC has four dual-core processors and high-end graphics cards.
Software: Open-source, some derived from gaming applications

The high-growth, or "worst-case," scenarios assume the same growth in world populations, but with economies still heavily reliant on fossil fuels. The high-growth scenarios predict carbon dioxide concentrations doubling by the year 2100 and temperatures increasing anywhere from 3.0 to 4.0°C (5.4 to 7.2°F). These numbers may be even higher, however, as the 2007 scenarios were based on rates of carbon dioxide emissions increasing more slowly than they actually did from 2007 to 2012.

No matter which scenario actually happens, Earth's temperatures are on the way up. This is not a good thing for anyone on Earth, whether they live by the ocean or not. This is why Jim Hack and others are cautioning us to start responding now to the challenge of climate change.

Check for Understanding

- What is a climate model?
- How are the low-growth and high-growth climate scenarios different?
- Describe the climate-change effect of the low-growth and high-growth scenarios.

Responding to Climate Change

Jim Hack would be the first person to tell you that climate models are complicated and that they are still being refined. But he does not have any doubts about the reality of climate change. If you sit down with him, he will show you data and more data, all of which confirm for him and his colleagues that the climate models are correct and that Earth is getting warmer. The question now is whether the world is listening to the scientists and the data.

Temperature reconstructions for the past 2,000 years, based on different types of data, all show similar patterns of temperature change over time. A report published in early 2013 looked at temperatures going back to the end of the last glacial event some 11,000 years ago. Temperatures rose as the glaciers melted, but had been falling for the last 5,000 years — until the beginning of the 20th century when temperatures started to increase and then climb rapidly.

The current climate models' short-term forecasts have been proven accurate. More often than not, the models have been too optimistic. Only the passing of the next 100 to 200 years

Expedition 3: Climate Change — Models and Decisions • 111

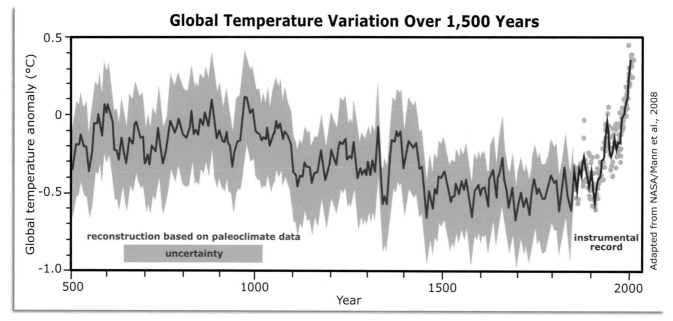

Global Temperature Variation Over 1,500 Years

Global temperature anomaly (°C)

reconstruction based on paleoclimate data

uncertainty

instrumental record

Year

Adapted from NASA/Mann et al., 2008

▲ This graph shows a rapid increase in average global temperatures in the last 100 years. The curve gets even steeper in the last 35 years. Where will this graph go from here?

will finally prove or disprove whether the models are accurate in their long-term forecasts. Carbon remains in the atmosphere for such a long time that to slow down the rate of climate change would require serious and immediate action. What then has been done in the past and what is being done right now to reduce human emissions of greenhouse gases?

International Efforts

Climate change is a worldwide concern. The inhabitants of this planet — humans, animals, plants — share the same atmosphere with the same greenhouse gases. It only makes sense that it would take agreements between all or many of the world's nations to bring about change that could address such a global issue.

The first international treaty on climate change was not even meant to be about climate change. In 1987, countries of the world adopted a treaty called the Montreal Protocol to reduce chemicals in the atmosphere that were destroying Earth's ozone layer. Those chemicals were also greenhouse gases, meaning that their reduction — and the Montreal Protocol — actually helped slow global warming.

The Kyoto Protocol was adopted in 1997. In this treaty, developed nations of the world pledged to reduce their greenhouse gas emissions by an average of 5% by 2012. Different countries had different emissions targets. As of December 2012, 190 nations plus the European Union had signed the Kyoto agreement. The United States signed the protocol, but did not ratify the treaty.

Subsequent United Nations climate summits have had limited success. The United States, China, and several other countries drafted something called the Copenhagen Accord, which they presented at the 2009 UN climate summit. This document states that climate change is one of today's greatest challenges and that all countries should take actions to keep Earth's global average temperature from increasing more than 2°C (3.6°F). This document was never formally adopted.

Why Is It So Difficult?

Change is always hard. Big changes are harder still. Making the tough decisions that could drastically cut greenhouse gas emissions and do it quickly enough to prevent runaway global warming are, by far, much tougher than most tough decisions.

Many stakeholders have an interest in addressing climate change: national, state, and local governments, major corporations, public utilities, small businesses, politicians, and regular citizens. The interests of different groups are not always the same, which can make it even more difficult to make decisions about an already complex issue.

To begin with, there are economic and political considerations, both within individual countries as well as globally. What are the costs of changing to cleaner energy? Will it cause job losses or harm the overall economy? Internationally, how do developing countries afford to modernize while choosing what are often more expensive technologies needed to reduce emissions?

Climate scientists around the world are in almost 100% agreement on climate change. They report their findings in terms of "percent likelihood" of something happening. To the public or to climate-change skeptics, this sounds like uncertainty. Scientists mean something different by certainty. Scientists tell us that they have very high certainty that carbon dioxide increases the greenhouse effect, that carbon dioxide levels in the atmosphere are rising rapidly, that air and ocean temperatures are increasing at an alarming rate, that sea levels are rising, and that glaciers and permafrost are melting. Jim Hack and his colleagues are saying that they have very high certainty that actions need to be taken soon to control greenhouse gas emissions, and if we are to slow down the rate of global warming.

What You Can Do

Much of what Earth's inhabitants have to do to reduce global warming needs to happen on a large scale. One important goal for industrialized societies is to reduce their greenhouse gas emissions by moving from carbon-based fuels to cleaner energy, such as solar, wind, hydroelectric, tidal, geothermal, and even nuclear power. Germany, for example, is already getting 22% of its energy from renewable sources, including about 5% of its electricity from solar panels. Bavaria, a state in southern Germany, has more installed solar capacity than the entire United States. The difference is that the German government has made it an official goal for the country to move toward renewable, low-carbon energy as quickly as possible, and has backed

You Can . . .

Reduce your own carbon footprint.

Use less. Eat foods that are processed less or are grown locally. Turn out the lights and switch to energy-efficient bulbs. Walk or ride a bike instead of drive. Use reusable water bottles. Anything you can do to use less energy will put less carbon into the air.

Encourage action within your community.

Where does your school's electricity come from? Some towns have gotten grants to help pay to install photovoltaics on school roofs. Get together with teachers and friends to see if that is possible where you live.

Lobby your elected representatives.

Join with your classmates to call or write your local, state, and federal government representatives. Get their position on climate change. Lobby for mass transit and clean energy in new public projects.

Help spread accurate information.

You cannot do anything about the millions of dollars spent each year denying climate change. You can, however, explain what you know and how you know it. A cold day in May does not disprove global warming and you can explain why.

up that decision with policies and incentives that encourage businesses and individuals to change old habits.

In the United States, there has been some progress in using less energy by promoting the use of more fuel-efficient cars. Some power plants have switched from burning coal to burning natural gas, a cleaner-burning fossil fuel that results in about half the carbon dioxide per unit of generated electricity. Not content to wait for national policy, California has announced state-wide goals to reduce greenhouse gas emissions to 1990 levels by the year 2020 and to get emissions 80% below 1990 levels by 2050.

That is what nations and states can do. On a much smaller scale, individuals can and should work to lower their carbon footprints. A **carbon footprint** is the amount of carbon dioxide released into Earth's atmosphere due to the consumption of fossil fuels by a particular person.

Climate change is a huge problem and one that often seems too large for anyone to do anything about. However, small efforts by many individuals can make a difference. Take Clearfield Middle School in Clearfield, Pennsylvania,

for example. That school switched one of its two boilers from burning natural gas to burning renewable wood chips. Not only is it costing the school district over $100,000 less per year to heat the building, but the boiler is releasing 50,000 kg (110,000 lb) less carbon dioxide into the atmosphere each year.

Or look at Alcoa Middle School in Alcoa, Tennessee. Kids there participated in a carbon footprint project in 2011, along with six other schools in Indiana, Ohio, Tennessee, and Virginia. About 8,000 students were able to find over 6,500,000 kg (14,400,000 lb) of carbon savings, just from encouraging their families to do things like recycling bottles and unplugging their printers and chargers when not in use.

Check for Understanding

- What are ways that nations can reduce greenhouse gas emissions?
- What are ways in which individual citizens can reduce their carbon footprint?

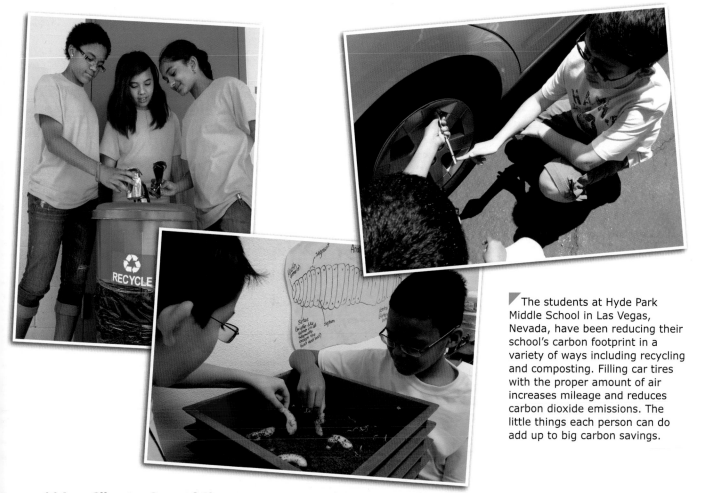

The students at Hyde Park Middle School in Las Vegas, Nevada, have been reducing their school's carbon footprint in a variety of ways including recycling and composting. Filling car tires with the proper amount of air increases mileage and reduces carbon dioxide emissions. The little things each person can do add up to big carbon savings.

STEM Spotlight

Mike Biddle

Career: Chemical Engineer
Born: Louisville, KY
Education: B.S., University of Louisville, Louisville, KY
Ph.D., Case Western Reserve University, Cleveland, OH

Mike Biddle could tell you a thing or two about waste. For example, not all garbage is the same. Metals, such as steel and aluminum, are easy to separate from trash and then recycle. But plastics have always been a lot more difficult to recycle. "The different plastics have very similar properties. And any kind of plastic can be any color. So, for plastics, the traditional ways of separating materials simply don't work." And when plastics cannot be sorted out and recycled, they become waste that most often ends up buried in a landfill or burned in an incinerator.

Biddle has been working hard to change all of that. He and his company, MBA Polymers, a member of the Institute of Scrap Recycling Industries (ISRI), found a way to separate and reclaim plastics in the waste stream and turn the waste plastic into new plastic. Biddle's company produces high-quality plastics from such things as discarded computers and car parts. As an added bonus, the plastics Biddle reclaims take 80% less energy to create than making new plastic from petroleum.

For Biddle, eliminating waste makes good environmental and business sense. "I believe that people want to act in a more responsible way and not waste materials and energy resources. My job is to make it easy for them to act that way and to convince them that what they do will make a difference."

Biddle on a pile of "shredder residue" — the raw material his recycling process separates into reusable plastics

Q & A

Did you always want to be an engineer?
I was interested in math and science but I didn't know what an engineer was. Then, when I was still in high school, I was working as a bus boy with an older boy who was already in college and studying engineering. We were talking and he told me that he thought I was "a natural engineer."

What personal traits make you suited for your job?
I have a natural curiosity about the world and how things work. Working on something I care about is not really work — it's fun. Yes, sometimes it can be very difficult and frustrating, like a homework problem you can't figure out right away. But the "aha!" moment when you finally figure it out is exciting.

What career accomplishments are you most proud of?
I am most proud of how we have invented, designed, built, and now operate the most advanced plastics recycling plants in the world — and that we've shown the whole world that this is possible.

What is the most exciting or scary thing that has happened to you in your work?
That would be when I gave my TED talk to a live audience of 1,000 people. There was only the one take. I needed for it to be "the talk of my life" for it "go live" on the TED website. I worked hard and practiced — and it paid off. That talk has been viewed by more than a million people, all over the world.

Reduce Your Carbon Footprint

Recall that your expedition goal is to investigate the causes and impacts of climate change and learn how scientists are working to predict Earth's climate future. Now that you have been fully briefed, you will apply what you have learned to take action to lessen your own impact on climate change. Jim Hack and other climate scientists are urging governments and individuals to take measures to reduce the greenhouse emissions that are contributing to climate change. The climate models that Hack runs show a need for action, but laws, regulations, and behaviors can be slow to change.

The fossil fuels that contribute to climate change are a part of our everyday lives. Most of the electricity we use comes from coal or natural gas. We use gasoline from a fossil fuel every time we ride in a car. And fossil fuels are used in the creation and transportation of the packaging that covers the food, drinks, and other goods we buy. The total greenhouse emissions caused by your activities and the choices you make are your carbon footprint. A great many factors go into making up an individual, group, or event's carbon footprint.

In this field assignment, you will look closely at your school's carbon footprint with a goal of reducing it. You will design an investigation to gather data about how one particular activity or part of the school contributes greenhouse gases to the atmosphere. Then you will develop a plan to reduce those greenhouse gas emissions and create a presentation to persuade key stakeholders to put your plan into action.

Expedition Challenge

- Develop a questionnaire to learn more about how one part of your school contributes greenhouse gases to the atmosphere.
- Identify one factor in your school's carbon footprint to reduce.
- Design and conduct an investigation to determine the greenhouse gas emissions from that factor.
- Develop a plan to reduce your school's greenhouse gas emissions from that factor.
- Create a presentation to persuade key stakeholders to put your plan into action.

Materials
- **items needed for your specific investigation**
- **presentation materials**

Part 1: Examine Your School's Carbon Footprint

1. Using what you have learned from *Climate: Seas of Change*, list some specific ways humans contribute greenhouse gases to the atmosphere. Brainstorm some ways your school in particular contributes greenhouse gases to the atmosphere.

2. Select one part of your school to focus on. For example, you might focus on the cafeteria, the classrooms, or the outdoor areas of the school. Come up with a list of things you do not know about this part of your school that could affect your school's carbon footprint. Refer to the list you made in step 1 for ideas of questions to ask.

3. Develop a questionnaire for your school's staff, to get more information about this part of your school and to identify ways it adds to the school's carbon footprint. If possible, interview key staff members to get the answers to your questions. Alternatively, send them the questionnaire and ask them to return their questions to you.

4. Once you have responses to your questionnaire, narrow your focus to one specific factor that contributes to your school's carbon footprint.

Part 2: Design an Investigation and Gather Data

1. Design an investigation to gather as much information as you can about the greenhouse gas emissions related to your chosen factor.

2. Get approval for your investigation from your teacher, and then conduct your investigation. Be sure to take specific measurements and keep good records. The data you collect will be useful in later parts of this Field Assignment.

③ Once your investigation is complete, use tables or graphs to organize and display your data.

④ Look at the data you gathered. Do you see any patterns? Where or when are greenhouse gas emissions highest? What are some of the biggest contributors to greenhouse gases in the area you investigated?

Part 3: Create an Action Plan

① Make a list of ways you could reduce greenhouse gas emissions for the factor you investigated. Reference the data from your investigation to identify the ways to reduce emissions that would have the biggest impact.

② Identify the stakeholders who would be involved in implementing any changes to this area of your school. Stakeholders are all the people on whom the changes you propose would have an impact and who therefore should have a say. Some stakeholders may include students, teachers, the school principal, custodial staff, cafeteria staff, etc.

③ If possible, share your list with key stakeholders to identify which ideas would work best.

④ Select one of your ideas and develop a plan to make it happen. Be very specific. Who has to take action? What actions do they have to take? When do they need to act? Consider all the stages necessary for your plan to work.

⑤ Analyze your plan by considering questions like: How much will it cost to put the plan into action? Where could that money come from? Who will benefit from this action? Who might be negatively affected by the plan? Create a cascading consequences chart to better understand how the action you wish to take would impact stakeholders. If necessary, refine your plan based on your analysis.

⑥ Discuss your plan with key stakeholders. Revise your plan based on their input.

Part 4: Develop a Persuasive Presentation

① Make a list of the concerns voiced by stakeholders or concerns you think they may have. For each concern, list ideas for how to respond to that concern.

② Discuss how you will persuade stakeholders to support your plan. Who are you trying to persuade? What will you need to communicate to them? How can you use the data gathered in your investigation to support your points? What visuals will best communicate the need for the action you wish to take?

③ Decide on a format for a presentation to persuade key stakeholders to support your action plan. You may decide to speak to them directly, using posters, brochures, or other visuals to back up your points. You may decide to incorporate technology, such as a PowerPoint presentation, into your presentation. You may choose to produce a video presentation, or come up with a format of your own. Whatever format you choose, be sure it is an effective way to communicate to the stakeholders you must persuade.

④ Create an outline for your presentation. Be sure to consider the items on the lists you made in step 1. Include specific data from your investigation to help support your points.

⑤ Create your presentation and share it with stakeholders.

Expedition Debrief

① Detail the revisions you made to your plan based on your analysis and the input of stakeholders.

② Was your persuasive presentation able to increase support for your plan? Describe your evidence and the outcome.

③ What additional data could you have collected to make the message of your presentation stronger?

④ How will you track the progress of your action plan over time?

⑤ How will you measure the effectiveness of your action plan?

Journal Question

How can actions taken by individuals and communities help to make a difference in dealing with climate change?

Join the Argonaut Adventure!

Work with and learn from the greatest scientists and engineers in the world as they engage in today's most exciting research, exploration, and conservation activities. JASON is always looking for motivated students and educators to join the JASON Argonaut adventure. Find out how you can be part of the team!

JASON National Argonaut Program

Each year, JASON selects a team of Host Researchers, students, and educators to participate in the JASON National Argonaut Program. Together, they conduct cutting-edge research and exploration in laboratories and field locations around the world. To learn more about the JASON National Argonauts and Host Researchers for *Climate: Seas of Change*, go to the JASON website to read their bios and view the Meet the Researcher videos.

Host Researchers

Katy Croff Bell
Chief Scientist, *Nautilus* Exploration Program
Old Lyme, CT
Expedition 1

Growing up on the Pacific coast, Katy Croff Bell came by her interest in the ocean honestly. Now she regularly sets sail on research expeditions around the world, where she and teams of researchers use cutting-edge technology to explore the ocean depths.

Diane Stanitski
Program Manager, NOAA Office of Climate Observation
Silver Spring, MD
Expedition 2

Diane Stanitski manages a global network of data-gathering buoys and drifters that tell scientists about the state of Earth's ocean in real time. Stanitski has also written three "Teacher at Sea" books for middle school students.

Jim Hack
Director, National Center for Computational Sciences, Oak Ridge National Laboratory
Oak Ridge, TN
Expedition 3

Jim Hack discovered his interest in weather when he was in sixth grade. Now he is in charge of a laboratory housing some of the world's fastest and most powerful computers, and uses them to run the complex models that predict Earth's climate future.

Educator Argonauts

Jason Pittman
Lorton, VA
Expedition 1

Jason Pittman became president of his own successful Internet design studio soon after graduating from college, but realized that his fulfillment came from making sacrifices in order to serve. He changed careers and became a teacher to help students achieve in science.

Lucinda Reese
South Bend, IN
Expedition 1

Lucinda Reese's grandmother instilled in her the importance of getting an education. She learned at an early age that she could really be and do whatever she wanted in life, as long as she worked for it. Her passion is educating children in science at the Boys & Girls Club.

Lisa Conselatore
Fairfax County, VA
Expedition 2

Lisa Conselatore has traveled around the world and has spent many years living abroad. She loves taking her students on outdoor adventures to inspire the spirit of curiosity and inquisitiveness in them.

Melinda Woods-Carpenter
Summersville, WV
Expedition 3

Melinda Woods-Carpenter's inspiration to pursue science came from her 8th-grade science teacher. She hopes her experience with JASON will help her inspire her students to pursue careers in science.

Student Argonauts

Devyn Jackson
Granger, IN
Expedition 1

Devyn has loved and played basketball since she was a young child and has played in tournaments year-round. She is also in the school leadership program and volunteers at the Boys & Girls Club.

Tashawn Reese
South Bend, IN
Expedition 1

Tashawn's love of marine biology was born at an ROV competition, and his dream is to one day become a marine biologist to view the deepest depths of the ocean.

Erin Walsh
Southlake, TX
Expedition 1

Erin has a strong passion for protecting the environment. She also plays the harp and was part of her school's Robotics and Engineering Club.

Marcelo Ancira
Monterrey, Mexico
Expedition 2

Marcelo is an active boxer and swimmer, and is a skilled cattle roper. Marcelo loves the interdisciplinary nature of science and is particularly interested in the field of biotechnology.

Sarah Mullins
Pennsboro, WV
Expedition 2

Sarah runs track and enjoys participating in drama and volunteering at a local food pantry. Her interest in science has grown stronger over the past few years, and she particularly enjoys the science of weather.

Keiana Yasunaka
Seaview, WA
Expedition 2

Keiana excels at both volleyball and basketball. Computer science camp sparked her interest in science and technology.

Dean Taylor
Golden, CO
Expedition 3

Dean's talents have led to his success as a guitar player and band performer. Dean enjoys a variety of science investigations and is especially fascinated with atomic structure.

Kate Burnett
Prosser, WA
Expedition 3

Kate enjoys volunteering and teaching music and ballet to young children. Kate has a natural curiosity for the world around her, which has led to her ambition to become a biologist.

Karthik Uppaluri
Mesa, AZ
Expedition 3

Karthik is a competitive swimmer, participates in robotics, and plays the violin. Karthik's passion for science and interest in astronomy drive his desire to experiment and learn more about the universe.

You are an Argonaut, too!

What are your interests? What would you want to tell other people about yourself? What do you like most about being part of the JASON community?

Are you interested in becoming a National Argonaut yourself and working with the next group of JASON Host Researchers? Check the JASON website to learn about the next opportunity and how to apply!

Begin your Argonaut Adventure at www.jason.org

Glossary

abyssal hill an undersea mountain that is shorter than 1 km (0.6 mi)

abyssal plain very flat area of the deep-ocean basin

air pressure the force per unit area exerted on a surface by the weight of the air above that surface

albedo the measure of how much sunlight is reflected by a substance on or above Earth's surface

arid lacking moisture; an arid climate does not have enough rainfall to grow trees or woody plants

asthenosphere a semi-solid layer of Earth's mantle that is located just below the lithosphere and that yields to high temperature and pressure by slowly flowing and shifting over time

atmosphere the layers of gases that surround Earth, which includes the layers called the troposphere, stratosphere, mesosphere, and thermosphere

bathymetric map a type of contour map that shows the topography of the ocean floor

black smoker a type of hydrothermal vent that gives the appearance of releasing black smoke into the water

buffer a substance that can either tie up or release hydrogen ions in order to maintain a solution's pH within a certain range

buoy a floating object, anchored to a river, lake, or ocean bottom, and used to show navigable channels or obstructions in a body of water; scientists also use buoys to place floating data-gathering instruments in areas of interest

carbon cycle the continuous process by which carbon is exchanged between living organisms and the environment

carbon dioxide a colorless, odorless gas found in Earth's atmosphere; the chemical formula is CO_2

carbon footprint the amount of carbon dioxide released into Earth's atmosphere due to the consumption of fossil fuels by a particular person

carbon sink something that absorbs more carbon than it releases

carbon source something that releases more carbon than it absorbs

climate the average weather conditions for a location over a long period of time

climate change any significant change in the climate lasting for an extended period of time

climate model a set of mathematical formulas used to describe how different variables affect Earth's climate

climate zone a division of Earth according to average temperatures and rainfall and the living things that are found there

condensation the act of matter changing state from gas to liquid, caused by the loss of heat energy in the gas

conduction the transfer of heat energy between atoms and molecules within the same object or between two objects that are touching

continental crust the layer of granitic, sedimentary, and metamorphic rocks that forms the continents and continental shelves; continental crust rock is less dense than oceanic crust rock

continental glacier a large, thick sheet of ice covering a large part of a continent; same as ice sheet

continental margin the area of relatively shallow water closest to the continents; it is made up of three parts: the continental shelf, the continental slope, and the continental rise

continental rise irregular surface found at the base of the continental slope; it separates the continental slope from the abyssal plain

continental shelf the shallowest part of the ocean floor and the closest to the shoreline

continental slope the sloping surface seaward of the continental shelf

convection the transfer of heat energy that occurs by material movement within a fluid

convergent boundary the region where two tectonic plates move into one another

coral bleaching the whitening of corals due to stress-induced loss of their symbiotic zooxanthellae

Coriolis effect the apparent deflection of movement from an expected straight path due to Earth's rotation

crust the thin and solid outermost layer of Earth that is rocky with relatively low density

current a large stream of moving water that moves within a larger body of water

deep-ocean basin the seafloor beneath the deep-ocean water; the deep-ocean basin is the part of the ocean that lies beyond the continental rise

deep-ocean current a density current caused by water masses with different temperatures and/or salinities; same as thermohaline current

deep water layer the cold water found below the thermocline

deforestation the large-scale removal of trees for farming, timber, or other land use

density a physical property of matter defined as the ratio of mass per unit volume

density current a current caused by gravity acting on two fluids of different densities; the fluid with greater density sinks below the fluid with lesser density

desert a dry climate area that receives so little rainfall that barely any vegetation can grow

divergent boundary the region where two tectonic plates move away from each other (e.g., the mid-ocean ridge)

doldrums a belt of light winds located near the equator

drought a prolonged period of below-normal rainfall over a large geographic area, having severe effects, such as crop loss and wildfires

dry climate a climate zone where the precipitation that falls to Earth from clouds has a good chance of being completely taken back up into the air again by evaporation and transpiration; dry climates can be either hot or cold

――――――――――― E ―――――――――――

eccentricity the noncircular shape of Earth's orbit

eddy the movement of a small current of water that is opposite the main current flow, forming a small, ring-shaped counter-current

El Niño the periodic flow of unusually warm surface water from the western Pacific Ocean toward the west coast of South America

elevation an object's height above sea level

energy budget the rough balance between the amount of energy that enters the Earth system from the sun and the amount of energy that leaves the system

engineering branch of science that applies mathematical, technical, and scientific knowledge to invent new technology

equator an imaginary circle drawn around Earth's middle at latitude 0°; the equator is equidistant from the poles and divides Earth into the Northern and Southern Hemispheres

evaporation the act of matter changing state from liquid to gas, caused by the gain of heat energy in the liquid

――――――――――― F ―――――――――――

fathom a unit of ocean water depth equal to 6 ft (1.83 m)

feedback loop in a system, something that is both an output of the system and an input that feeds back into the system; in climate change, a positive feedback loop accelerates the warming trend and a negative feedback loop decelerates it

flood any unusually high flow, overflow, or inundation by water that causes damage or threatens to cause damage

fossil fuel a natural material, such as coal, petroleum, or natural gas, which formed from the remains of living organisms in Earth's distant past and which can be burned for energy

――――――――――― G ―――――――――――

glacial the colder period of an ice age when ice sheets advance

glacial erratic a rock that is different in composition from nearby rocks because it has been transported a great distance from its place of origin by a glacier

glacier a large, long-lived accumulation of ice, snow, liquid water, and sediment originating on land that moves down-slope under the influence of its own weight and gravity

global ocean conveyor a system of water circulation that connects the ocean's surface currents with its thermohaline (deep-ocean) currents: the global ocean conveyor transports heat from the tropics to the poles and greatly influences Earth's climate

global warming the gradual increase in air temperatures near Earth's surface

greenhouse effect the trapping of heat near the planet's surface by gases in the atmosphere

greenhouse gas an atmospheric gas that absorbs heat, such as water vapor, carbon dioxide, and methane

Gulf Stream a warm ocean surface current that flows northward along the eastern coast of North America

gyre a large, oval-shaped system of ocean surface current loop; gyres rotate clockwise in the Northern Hemisphere and counterclockwise in the Southern Hemisphere

――――――――――― H ―――――――――――

heat the energy associated with the motion of atoms or molecules that can be transmitted by conduction, convection, and radiation; same as thermal energy

highlands climate the cold, harsh climate zone that occurs at high elevations, on top of tall mountains and mountain ranges

hurricane a large, low-pressure, tropical cyclone with sustained wind speeds greater than 119 km/h (74 mph)

hydrothermal vent a place where ocean water seeps down into the seafloor, gets heated up and enriched in minerals by magma that is close to the seafloor surface, and then circulates back out into the ocean from cracks in Earth's crust

――――――――――― I ―――――――――――

ice age a long period of time in which the climate cools enough that continental glaciers form and advance

ice cap a polar climate area and the most extreme climate on Earth; the ice cap is a thick mass of ice and snow, covering a wide area; an ice cap is smaller than an ice sheet

ice sheet a large, thick sheet of ice covering a large part of a continent; same as continental glacier

interglacial the warmer period of an ice age separating two glacials

ion an atom or group of atoms that has either a positive or negative charge due to the loss or gain of one or more electrons

──────────── J ────────────

jet stream a narrow band of very strong, westerly winds that blow at high altitudes in the middle latitudes

──────────── K ────────────

kettle pond a pond formed in the depression left in an outwash plain in front of a retreating continental glacier when a buried block of ice melts

──────────── L ────────────

La Niña the periodic cooling of the surface water in the eastern and central Pacific Ocean

latent heat heat released or absorbed by a substance during a change in the state of matter, such as water going from solid ice to liquid water

latitude measurement of distance north or south of the equator

leeward the side away from the wind; the leeward side of an object, such as a mountain or building, is protected from the oncoming wind

lithosphere the solid layer of rock that includes Earth's crust and the uppermost part of the mantle

longitude measurement of distance east or west of the prime meridian

──────────── M ────────────

magma molten rock beneath Earth's surface

mantle the layer of Earth situated below the crust and above the outer core

methane a colorless and odorless gas formed from the remains of animals and plants; also known as natural gas

microclimate a local area where the climate differs from the surrounding climate

Mid-Atlantic Ridge the part of the mid-ocean ridge that runs north to south down the middle of the Atlantic Ocean

mid-ocean ridge a continuous range of underwater mountains that forms where Earth's tectonic plates gradually move apart (or diverge)

mixed layer the near-surface layer of the ocean where the water is heated by the sun and mixed by the motions of waves and tides so that the temperature and salinity of the water is fairly uniform

──────────── O ────────────

ocean acidification the ongoing decrease in the pH of Earth's ocean, caused by the absorption of excess carbon dioxide from Earth's atmosphere

oceanic crust the rocks that form the ocean basin; oceanic crust is denser and thinner than continental crust

oceanography the branch of science dealing with the physical, chemical, geological, and biological features of the ocean, the ocean basin, and the water in the ocean

──────────── P ────────────

perihelion the point in Earth's oval orbit when Earth is closest to the sun

permafrost a layer of permanently frozen soil

pH the measure of a solution's acidity; pH measures the hydrogen ion concentration of a solution

plate tectonics theory that slabs of Earth's lithosphere (tectonic plates) move around on the putty-like asthenosphere, moving apart or colliding to form ocean basins, mountains, and new continents

polar climate the coldest climate zone that occurs at or near Earth's poles and includes the tundra and ice cap climates

polar easterlies cold, dry winds that blow from east to west around the polar regions; the polar easterlies are located between approximately 60° and 90° latitude in both hemispheres

precession a change in the orientation of the axis of a rotating body, such as Earth; Earth's precession affects when perihelion occurs

prevailing westerlies bands of wind blowing from west to east and located between approximately 30° and 60° latitude in both hemispheres

──────────── R ────────────

radiation the direct transfer of energy by electromagnetic waves

rift a linear zone of volcanic activity and faulting of Earth's crust caused by diverging tectonic plates and tension forces

──────────── S ────────────

Saharan Air Layer a hot, dry, dusty air layer that forms over North Africa in the summer and affects the formation of hurricanes in the Atlantic Ocean

salinity a measurement of the amount of dissolved material or salts in a liquid; salinity is typically measured in parts per thousand (ppt)

salt a chemical compound that dissolves in water to form ions; table salt, or sodium chloride, is one example of a salt

savanna a tropical climate grassland that experiences seasonal rains

sea breeze a cool, local wind created by air moving from a high-pressure area over the ocean toward a low-pressure area over the land

sea level the average level of the ocean's surface where it strikes land at a specific location

seafloor the solid bottom surface beneath the ocean

seafloor spreading the formation of new seafloor crust at mid-ocean ridges as two diverging tectonic plates spread apart

seamount an undersea mountain usually formed by volcanic activity; a seamount is at least 1 km (0.6 mi) tall, but not tall enough to reach the ocean's surface

sediment solid pieces of rocks, minerals, or remains of plants or animals that vary in size and that can be transported by erosion

solar energy energy from the sun

sonar a system for measuring water depth and detecting objects under water by emitting sound pulses and measuring how long it takes for the pulses to return to the source

sounding a depth measurement or the process by which one measures the depth of the ocean or some other body of water

specific heat the amount of thermal energy needed to raise the temperature of 1 g of a substance by 1°C

STEM the acronym for science, technology, engineering, and mathematics

steppe a flat, dry climate area covered with grasses and short bushes; a steppe may border a desert, but is less dry

storm surge a large wave of water that is pushed onshore by wind; during a hurricane, the storm surge typically poses the greatest threat to life and property

subduction a geologic process where one tectonic plate sinks below a second, less dense tectonic plate as the two plates come together (or converge)

submarine canyon a steep-sided valley cut into the continental slope

submersible a type of vessel capable of operating or remaining under water, allowing scientists to explore and do research in deep water

sunspot dark, cool spot on the sun's surface

surface current a large stream of water moving along at the ocean's surface

───────── T ─────────

technology applied science for human advancement

tectonic plate a large slab of Earth's rigid lithosphere that moves over the more putty-like asthenosphere beneath

temperate continental climate a climate zone occurring at mid-latitudes, inside continents and away from the ocean; without the moderating effect of the ocean, this zone has larger temperature ranges between summer and winter and less rain during the year

temperate marine climate a climate zone occurring at mid-latitudes, on land near the ocean; temperate marine climates are affected by the nearby ocean; because the ocean moderates the temperature, the temperatures do not vary greatly with the seasons, leading to mild winters and cool summers

thermal expansion process by which matter tends to change its volume in response to a change in temperature

thermocline layer of water between the mixed layer above and the deep water layer below; water temperature rapidly decreases with water depth within the thermocline

thermohaline current a density current caused by water masses with different temperatures and/or salinities; same as deep-ocean current

trade winds steady, consistent winds blowing from east to west and located at approximately 30° latitude in both hemispheres

transpiration process by which water absorbed by plants, usually through their roots, is evaporated into the atmosphere from the plants' leaves

trench a long, narrow, deep depression in the ocean floor created by the subduction of a tectonic plate

tropical climate a climate zone where the average monthly temperature of the coldest month is more than 18°C (64°F) and precipitation is ample for more than half the year; the tropical climate zone includes the rainforest and savanna climates

tundra a polar climate area marked by its permafrost and lack of trees

turbidity a measurement of how cloudy or clear water is

turbidity current a type of density current, made of water and sediment, which can travel like an avalanche down the continental slope and carve submarine canyons

───────── U ─────────

upwelling the vertical movement of cold, nutrient-rich water from the deep ocean to the ocean's surface

urban heat island the observed effect of large cities on annual average air temperature; air temperatures in large cities are at least 1 to 3°C (1.8 to 5.4°F) warmer than those in the rural, less developed surrounding area

───────── W ─────────

waste heat the heat released by a machine or an electrical appliance that is energy wasted or lost to the system

watershed an area of land in which all water drains to a common outlet, such as a stream, a river, or the ocean

weather the condition of the atmosphere at a particular place and time; weather is measured in terms of temperature, humidity, air pressure, cloudiness, and precipitation

wind the horizontal movement of air from an area of high air pressure to an area of low air pressure

windward the side facing the wind; the windward side of an object, such as a mountain or building, is exposed to the oncoming wind

Credits

JASON Learning would like to acknowledge the many people who have made valuable contributions in the development of *Climate: Seas of Change.*